wired for influence

Skills to Lead Others

Tim Elmore

foreword by John Maxwell

LifeWay Press

Nashville, Tennessee

Published by:

Student Ministry Publishing

LifeWay Christian Resources

One LifeWay Plaza

Nashville, TN 37234-0174

Customer Service: (800) 458-2772

Order additional copies of this book

or other collegiate resources published by LifeWay by writing to Customer Service Center, MSN 113;

One LifeWay Plaza; Nashville, TN 37234-0113; by calling toll free (800) 458-2772;

by faxing (615) 251-5933; by ordering online at *www.lifeway.com*;

by emailing *customerservice@lifeway.com*; or by visiting a LifeWay Christian Store.

Printed in The United States of America

ISBN

EQUIP   Student Ministry Publishing
"Growing Leaders"   LifeWay Christian Resources
PO Box 1808   One LifeWay Plaza
Duluth, GA 30096   Nashville, TN 37234-0174

If you are teaching this in a group study and would like teaching helps,
you can find them electronically by going to *www.EQUIPorg.org/WFI*
or by contacting LifeWay Christian Resources at 615-251-2783 for a free hard copy.

As God works through us, we will help people and churches know Jesus Christ and seek His kingdom

by providing biblical solutions that spiritually transform individuals and cultures.

ontents

Acknowledgments

I have to thank the team of leaders that Student Ministry Publishing and National Collegiate Ministry at LifeWay Christian Resources brought together for their invaluable input in the creation of this resource. These men and women from all over the country shared their wisdom and experience in an effort to produce another great collegiate leadership tool possible for developing emerging leaders.

I also wish to thank Tracey Fries, my executive assistant, who helped me reach goals I could not have reached without help. She protects me and provides for me so that I can focus on creating resources.

Finally, I wish to thank my friend and EQUIP intern Aaron Ling, who labored with me to create this guide. He worked with diligence and detail until it was finished. Thanks, Aaron, for modeling the skills we try to communicate in this resource.

Foreword

by John Maxwell, founder of InJoy Ministries based in Atlanta, GA.

I love meeting young leaders at the conferences where I am speaking. I love their energy, their optimism, and their passion for accomplishing something great for God. I guess I love the fact that so many of them really believe they can change the world.

One of the common characteristics I have seen in collegiate leaders, however, is the vast amount of questions they have. When I get the chance to sit down and talk with college or seminary students, they usually have loads of questions about how they could lead more effectively. And it makes sense. Those young leaders are at the beginning of their leadership journey. They have so much yet to experience.

That's why this resource, *Wired For Influence*, is so vital. Tim Elmore created it to answer the fundamental questions you might have concerning your leadership role: how do I communicate God's vision more clearly, how do I establish my priorities, how do I recruit a good team and then release them to play the role they are best designed to play, and how do I lead when people become difficult and I want to quit? In short, *Wired For Influence* is a manual for you to begin your journey on the right foot. It covers the "nuts and bolts" of the leadership functions you will need to perform.

Let me encourage you to go through this book in a group. At EQUIP, and our newly founded division called, Growing Leaders, we have discovered a number of realities as we have attempted to equip student leaders all over the world:

1. Leaders are made, not born.
2. Every college student has leadership potential.
3. Collegians learn leadership best in communities.
4. Leadership development is a process, not an event.
5. In today's world, every college student will need to learn leadership.
6. College students need a coach to help them grow into effective leaders.

If you will commit to go through this book in a covenant/mentoring group, I believe you will find the interaction, the stories, the principles, and the assignments invaluable. The community and the accountability you'll experience will accelerate your growth.

I have known Dr. Tim Elmore, the author of this resource, for twenty years now. He has worked with me since 1983. I have had the privilege of mentoring him as he ministered to college students through those years. He is experienced as a leader. He is experienced as a writer. He is experienced as a minister to collegians.

My thanks as well to Student Ministry Publishing of LifeWay Church Resources for partnering with us to make this book possible for you. The first book in this series by Tim is entitled, *Authentic Influence: Leading Without Titles*, and provides the biblical foundation for Christian leadership. You may want to add this to your collegiate resources library. Both books can be obtained by contacting LifeWay at 1-800-458-2772.

Your Leadership Role

PRECIOUS TREASURE OR PERFORMANCE TRAP?

*"Come to me, all you who are weary and burdened,
and I will give you rest."*
—Matthew 11:28

*"By the grace of God I am what I am, and his grace to me was not without
effect. No, I worked harder than all of them—yet not I,
but the grace of God that was with me."*
—1 Corinthians 15:10

Freedom Fighters

I remember a trip I was on back in 1991. I was on board a flight returning home to San Diego. I distinctly remember one thing about that flight: it was full of Marines. After thinking about it for a moment I realized these soldiers were coming home from Operation Desert Storm. Intrigued, I engaged in conversation with one of the young men. I asked him if he was coming back from Kuwait, and he confirmed my suspicion. I then asked him what probably seemed like a strange question. "What was the highlight of your experience?" After thinking for a few minutes, he replied, "The highlight for me was knowing that I was playing a role in liberating an entire nation."

At the beginning of Desert Storm, the news on TV showed a very apprehensive Kuwaiti people. They questioned our motives. They wondered if we were there for the same reason the invading Iraqi army had come in months before. Within weeks, this changed. The Kuwaiti people started to like us. By the end of the war, they were hugging our soldiers and showing their thanks. They had finally realized that the Americans had come just to set them free.

Since that conversation, it has occurred to me that we react to God in the same way. Like Kuwait, many of us question what would happen if we let God into our lives. *What would He do? What would He want from us? Would He force us to do something we didn't want to do?*

Can you remember when it first occurred to you that God simply wanted to invade your life because He loved you? God did not save you because of what you can do for Him. He just wanted to come to set you free.

In this session we will evaluate the foundation upon which our lives and ministries are built. So often, in our pursuit of results, we slip into ministry motivated by guilt rather than grace. We feel as if God evaluates us based on our performance. My prayer is that this simple lesson will serve as a reminder of where our power and motivation for service really comes from.

Reflect and Respond ...

From what do you need to be set free? Write it here.

Basic Truth
Your service should be done from devotion, not duty.

Guided Prayer
Lord,
please prepare my heart for all that I am about to learn.

Help me to see that You do not love me for what I do but for who I am.

Reveal Your love to me and deepen my love for You.

Show me the best way to accomplish my ministry. In the name of Your Son,

Amen.

Encountering Jesus

Take a look at Luke 10:38-42. In it, we read of Jesus' early encounter with two sisters named Mary and Martha. They are a picture of contrasting approaches to God. In the passage they show us two ways we can react to Jesus when we first meet Him. Generally, we experience one of two drives when we encounter the Lord. Take a look below to see which one of these ambitions you are prone to experience.

> We are driven to get busy for Him. (Martha)

> We are driven to get close to Him. (Mary)

Martha and Mary are vivid illustrations of these two drives, or compulsions. Martha wanted to impress Jesus, so she attempted to perform for Him. Can't you just see her that night? She was so busy trying to serve the dinner for Jesus that she forgot where her power came from. Finally, she registered a complaint to Jesus. She asked Him to tell Mary to help her out. I am certain that she really wanted Jesus to notice all her hard work. Instead, He directed the attention to Mary. Mary determined she must first be served by Jesus before she attempted to serve Him. Mary made sure she was connected to Jesus before she tried to conquer anything for Him. She mastered the "following thing" before she tried the "leadership thing." In sitting at Jesus' feet, she both laid a foundation for future service as well as established pure motives for her future service.

Here is the point. There came a time when Mary did serve Jesus. She came to Him with an alabaster vase of expensive perfume and poured it over His feet. Then she wiped His feet with her hair! It was an extravagant act of service. Unlike Martha's performance, Jesus affirmed what Mary did. He said her service would be remembered forever! What a contrast! Jesus was just as interested in the motivation behind the service as He was the actual service. How does this measure up in your life?

Burn On or Burn Out

Katharine had recently become student body vice-president on her campus. When she started her position, she was full of passion; but pretty soon she found out that being vice-president could be tiresome and costly. She couldn't do all the things she wanted to do with her friends, many times she had to stay up later than she wanted, and often felt like she was sacrificing her schooling for her position. She was starting to burn out. Do you know anyone like Katharine? It took Katharine time to just sit down, and sort through her motives. Her relationship with Jesus had become a routine. She had to ask God to renew her passion. Restoring a passionate relationship is key to recovering strength. Take a look at the list below. Notice the differences between Mary and Martha. Where did Martha's strength come from?

MARTHA	MARY
1. Seeks approval on her terms	1. Seeks relationship with Him
2. Priority is "Doing"	2. Priority is "Being"
3. Acts out of duty	3. Acts out of devotion
4. Motivation is guilt	4. Motivation is gratitude
5. Offers no power	5. Offers unlimited power
6. Performance from a driven spirit	6. Service from a response to grace

"We find freedom when we find God; we lose it when we lose Him."
—Paul Scherer

Group Up
In what ways have you become similar to a Mary or a Martha?

This is a significant lesson because we live in a college culture that focuses on results and performance. We want to feel like we are doing something to accomplish the goal. With a mindset like that, it is very easy to slip into this trap. It is a **"performance trap."**

Being Before Doing

I saw a powerful example of this trap within my own ministry at Skyline Church in San Diego. One of my college students got stuck in this performance trap so much so he had to see a counselor. It didn't take long for the counselor to diagnose his problem. In only a few weeks she said to this young man, "I know what your problem is. You have become a human doing before you've become a human being." This phrase may sound like a cliche, but isn't it true for many of us today?

We need to understand that there is nothing wrong with activity, but our "doing" must be birthed from our "being." We must build a foundation of grace before we get busy leading anything. In fact, we will accomplish more once we are empowered by grace, like Mary, than we ever could do trying to produce results on our own.

Reflect and Respond ...

Do you think it is easier to be a Mary or a Martha? Share one or two reasons why you believe this.

I have attempted to break this subject into three parts: Our Problem, Our Potential, and Our Prescription. Below I have given you three points to consider. Let's first look at "our problem," and how it deals with this idea of performance vs. service.

Our Problem

Let's define what we mean by the terms *performance* and *service,* and as a result, define where our problem lies:

Performance. *Something done out of human obligation, contrived from human strength in order to gain the approval of others.*

Notice that performance is all about human effort and motives; it is horizontal, not vertical. It is done from human strength. This definition is where we get our sense of duty. Again, there is nothing wrong with a sense of duty, but if that's all we have, before too long we will run out of gas. I'm certain when Martha complained about having to prepare the dinner all by herself, she really wanted Jesus to affirm her. Step into her sandals for a moment. She would have loved to have heard Jesus say, "Oh my goodness, Martha. I had no idea you were doing all that work alone. Hey, everyone—do you see what Martha is doing? What a servant! Now, she needs some help! Mary, get yourself into the kitchen right now and help your sister!"

Group Up
Discuss within the group some of the pressures on you to perform in school, and how it has affected you.

But Jesus never said that to her. He wasn't impressed by her performance. Instead, He contrasted her fleshly performance with Mary's decision to sit at His feet. Her fleshly nature had masqueraded as spiritual service. On the outside it looked great, but Jesus knew what was really going on inside her heart. We can spot the symptoms when we choose to follow our fleshly desires. Take a look at the following list and see how Martha illustrated a performance mentality.

a. You become distracted from "big-picture" priorities, being consumed by your own performance.
b. You project your self worth to others and overestimate your importance.
c. You experience "self pity" and seek recognition for your hard work.
d. You grow weary because you attempt to do too much for the wrong reasons.
e. You tend to be a perfectionist.

Service. *Something done out of an experience of grace. It is a loving response to a new identity in order to say thank you to God.*

Almost everyone desires this lifestyle. Unfortunately, it's all too easy to move from a grace-centered service to a people-pleasing duty. This is not a new concept. Many people through the ages have struggled with it. In fact, when the apostle Paul wrote to the Galatians, he was addressing the exact same problem. In Galatians 2:15-16 Paul suggested that they were attempting to gain God's approval by working for it. He told them they had fallen from grace. The Galatians had slipped into the exact same trap. They were trying to please God by doing instead of being.

Reflect and Respond ...

If answered honestly, the three questions below can safeguard you from the performance trap. If you were to describe yourself related to these questions, jot down your answers:

What's behind my ministry?

Why do I do what I do?

What do I seek from doing ministry?

Performance vs. Service:
The Difference Between Law and Grace

I have listed the difference between performance and service. After looking at both lists, which one do you tend to experience the most as a leader on your campus?

PERFORMANCE	SERVICE
1. Striving in human strength	1. Acknowledges human weakness; waits on God's strength and timing
2. Bondage to law and legalism	2. Freedom to give out of devotion, not duty
3. Imbalance: more doing than being	3. Balanced rhythm of reflection and obedience
4. Motive is to please people	4. Ability to say no to people at God's direction
5. Comparison with others	5. Acceptance of others
6. Manipulate and control others	6. People free to make choices and be different
7. Lack of joy and peace	7. Experience the fruit of the Spirit
8. Extreme reactions	8. Consistency, stability; sensitive to His leading
9. Frustration with self	9. Acceptance of God's growth process in you
10. Relationship with God unstable	10. Slow but steady growth with God and vacillating
11. Work to gain God's approval	11. Natural life-response to God's previous, unconditional approval
12. Produces stronghold of religion	12. Produces deep relationship with God

Reflect and Respond ...

Share your impressions of what all the things on this list have in common. What are their differences?

The power to BE is a priority over the power to DO, because if you are SOMEONE, you will naturally do SOMETHING.

Group Up
What steps would you have to take in your life to accomplish these remedies?

Conclusions on Our Problem

1. Our ministry on campus must move from performance to service.
We need to take what we do out of our hands and put it into the hands of God.

2. We must make this move through a grace experience.
When we receive the grace of God, we realize that He loved us even before we could have done anything for Him. In fact, some of us need to experience this grace all over again.

3. We cannot be grace-givers unless we are grace-receivers.
We need to be filled up before we are able to give. For some of us that means we just need to let God love us.

"We love because he first loved us" (1 John 4:19).

Reflect and Respond ...

In your opinion, what is the reward for Christian service?

What is the reward for performance?

Our Potential

Experiencing God's grace enables us to live and serve on a higher level. When we invite Christ to be our Lord, we experience the grace to save us and take us to heaven. (I'd say that's living on a higher level!) However, many of us leave that posture of humility and attempt to grow by working for it.

If our ministry is going to be supernatural (as Jesus called it to be) we must realize that everything in God's kingdom comes by GRACE through faith. We must see and believe this before our lives will reflect it. Note the following three word pictures.

The Father and Son Analogy

The metaphor used most to describe God in the New Testament is not *King*, or *Creator*, or *Master of the Universe*. All of those are correct, but the term used most often is that of a Father. It is important for us to understand that God is a father to us before He is a taskmaster or an employer. We do work for Him; we do His work, but it is out of a Father-child relationship that it takes place. He is our Father, we are His children. The story of the prodigal son (Luke 15) is a beautiful picture of God as a Father, relating to His son out of grace.

At a speaking engagement in New York a few years ago, I saw a great picture of this kind of relationship. I was about to speak, when I looked out into the congregation and noticed a father and his son. The father was holding his son close to him, and in a few minutes I noticed why. The son was about nine years old, but he was very fidgety. He would squeak and make noises. I noticed that through all of this, the father did nothing to discipline him. The son would make noise and move around, and it was soon apparent that his behavior was going to be a distraction. I thought to myself, *I hope he's quiet during my message!* This went on for about fifteen minutes; all the time the father just held his son closer and closer to him. Then the father stood up, scooped his son in his arms, and carried him out of the service. Well, now I was hooked, and I just had to see what was going to happen to this little boy. When I slipped back to the foyer, I saw something that I will never forget. The father was sitting on a small chair, with his son in his arms, stroking his hair, and whispering, "I love you, son. You know I love you." I went to an usher nearby and asked him what was going on. His response explained everything. He told me the little boy was epileptic, and about every other Sunday he got a little noisy and fidgety. He then said, "You know, it's interesting. That father always knows what to do to calm him down."

Do you know what that father was doing? That father was giving grace to his son.

Sometimes in our lives we become spiritual epileptics. We distract people from God. We draw attention to ourselves. Yet, God always knows what to do to get us back on target. He too gives us grace.

Grace gives us supernatural power to do far more than the law has ever expected.

The law tells us what to do, but gives no way for us to overcome sin. With the law all we have is "thou shall not." Then we have to strive with all we have in our human effort to try to accomplish that. However, God, in His infinite wisdom, understands that what we need is grace, love, and unmerited favor. But grace is not just unmerited favor; it is unlimited power. In 2 Corinthians 12:9 Jesus spoke to Paul about his thorn in the flesh, and said, "My grace is sufficient for you, for my power is made perfect in weakness." In the past, many have interpreted this to mean God was just saying no. Really, God was saying, "Paul, you will be able to handle this and more if you get a dose of my grace."

A few years back I attended a conference in which a well-known Christian author decided to be very vulnerable. He shared with us that he traveled a lot. In fact, he was away from home so often that at one point he had made up his mind he was going to commit adultery. He was away on business, he had a female friend who lived in town, and he decided he would call her, and they would enjoy the night together.

When he got to the city, he checked into a hotel under a fictitious name. Once in his room, he reached for the phone to call his friend. However, when he started to dial the numbers, he was overwhelmed by the love of God. He hung up the phone and tried again. The same feeling came over him, but this time he was reminded of Bible verses. "How great is the love the Father has lavished on us, that we should be called children of God" (1 John 3:1). "Who shall separate us from the love of Christ?" (Rom. 8:35). "God so loved the world that he gave his one and only Son, that whoever believes in him shall not perish but have eternal life" (John 3:16). God simply poured into this man's heart Scriptures on His unconditional love.

The author slammed the phone down, determined to carry out this sin. When he started to dial the third time, God's love was overwhelming. This time it was felt more deeply than the first two. He slammed the phone down again, looked up, and cried, "God, it is no use! I am hopelessly in love with you!" That night he didn't sin. The grace of God gave him the strength to withstand the temptation of evil.

"As the earth can do nothing without being fertilized by the sun, so we can do nothing without the grace of God."
—Vianney

Group Up
If you are comfortable doing so, discuss ways that you need grace in your life right now.

Let me ask you a question: If you were God in that situation, how would you have handled this man? Wouldn't it have made more sense to yell from heaven: "Thou shalt not commit adultery"? It might have, but it would not have given this man any power to refrain. What he needed was grace.

The Marriage Analogy

We are the bride of Christ before we are the slave of Christ. Once married, a wife takes the name of her husband and has rights to all that he owns. In the same way, we have been married to Jesus and have access to all the grace and power we will ever need. Weddings are ceremonies that center on love more than duty. Husbands and wives don't stand at the altar and say, "I promise to take out the garbage and sweep the kitchen."

Unfortunately, that's how we sometimes treat God. We say, "Lord, come into my heart and I promise to pray, tithe, and go to church." And the whole time God responds by asking: "Will you just love Me? If you do that, you will do far more than duty will get you to do."

I have found this to be true in my own marriage. My wife loves ice cream, and we often go out to get ice cream. Nothing was in our wedding vows about my doing this for her. As we have fallen more in love, I find it a joy to do things for her and serve her. Jesus wants the exact same thing.

The Police Analogy

Have you heard the phrase on TV or in movies, "Stop, in the name of the law!"? Under what power did the police officer operate? We know that he is a representative of the government, and because of that, he has its backing and authority. Many times, when a stoplight at a busy intersection is malfunctioning, a police officer will direct traffic. One person controls several tons of cars. Does this person have the literal power to stop all of them? Of course not. But behind that officer's arm is the entire United States government. If we neglect to heed his warnings, we would soon be dealing with the National Guard instead of one officer!

This analogy is fitting for us, too. We are God's representatives and operate under His authority. With our own power and strength, we cannot do much. However, we don't serve in our own names. We serve in the name and authority of Jesus. By His authority we can do all things. He is the strength and motivation behind what we do!

One day Mother Teresa was visited by some dignitaries who had come to observe her mission work in Calcutta. At that time she was scrubbing down the skin of a leper, cleaning him. The dignitary looked down and snickered, "I wouldn't do that for a million dollars." Without a moment's hesitation, Mother Teresa looked up at him and replied, "I wouldn't either." Behind her service was not monetary compensation. She didn't get paid. Love and grace were her motives. We need the same motivation.

Reflect and Respond ...

What metaphor do you use most frequently concerning God in your ministry with other students?

"The law detects; grace alone conquers sin."
—St. Augustine

What is your motivation for leading right now?

Biblical Basis for a Grace-Empowered Ministry

In several passages of Scripture God expresses how crucial grace is to our leadership. Look at these verses and see if they give you a bit more insight.

2 Corinthians 9:8—"God is able to make all grace abound to you, so that in all things at all times, having all that you need, you will abound in every good work."

2 Corinthians 12:9—"He said to me, 'My grace is sufficient for you, for my power is made perfect in weakness.'"

Ephesians 2:8-10—"It is by grace you have been saved, through faith—and this not from yourselves, it is the gift of God—not by works, so that no one can boast. For we are God's workmanship created in Christ Jesus to do good works, which God prepared in advance for us to do."

1 Corinthians 15:10—"By the grace of God I am what I am, and his grace to me was not without effect. No, I worked harder than all of them—yet not I, but the grace of God that was with me."

Our Prescription

What steps must we take to return to a "grace lifestyle"? Let's begin with the following applications for our campus ministry:

Our "Mary" experience should precede our "Martha" experience.

We must find a balance rhythm of "being" and "doing."

We must believe and embrace these "grace" foundations.

Grace Foundations

1. God's grace is mine for free because it's based on Jesus' performance, not mine.
There is no work that we can do that will merit the death and resurrection of Christ on the cross. It's all based on His performance, not mine. Because of His works we are saved and receive grace.

2. God does not love me and save me for what I can do for Him.
This point is the same with marriage. We don't marry someone for what they can do, but because we love them. God, the self-sufficient One, allows us to work with Him because He loves us not because we can do things. It is all based on love.

Group Up

Discuss ways you have seen the difference between someone who was grace-powered and one who was man-powered.

3. I must die to my "old husband" (the law) and stop relating to God on that basis.
The law seldom relates to us in a positive way. It can only tell us what we are doing wrong. God wants to empower us through grace. The law was given to us as a guide, but does not provide the power to do anything

4 God's grace accepts me as I am, then enables me to live above my own ability.
God loves us just the way we are, but He loves us too much to leave us that way. The grace He gives to us is to help us live a new, supernaturally powered life.

5. The only requirement for receiving grace is humility.
We need to admit that within ourselves we have no power, and that only with Christ can we live. James 4:6 reminds us that God opposes the proud, but gives grace to the humble.

6. My service is actually greater under grace, because gratitude, not guilt, is the motivation.
The joy that we have encourages us to do more. The power that grace provides enables us to do more. Many times, the more we do because of gratitude, the more joy we find.

Stepping into Grace

If you have been saying to yourself through this lesson that you may be falling into this trap, I would like to give you these seven steps:

Reveal—Seek honest personal examination and diagnosis.
Ask yourself where you are right now. How do you relate to God?

Relinquish—Surrender my performance issues to God.
Name areas that you need to release to God, then surrender to God.

Recall—Note the people and issues for which I am performing.
What are you doing, or who are you around when you fall into this trap?

Release—Forgive; let go of wrong views and surrender myself.
There may be resentment in your life. Let it go. Forgive both yourself and others.

Request—Ask the Holy Spirit to reveal (dispense) God's grace.
This is the power step. Asking for grace is not a one-time experience. We need to daily ask for grace in our situations.

Renounce—Refuse to allow wrong motives to rule me.
Say aloud what it is that you would like to get rid of in your life.

Respond—Return to serving God from a loving, responsive heart.
This list is incomplete without this step. You need to return to your ministry not with just head knowledge about grace, but with overflowing power from it.

A story from early Christian history sold me on this idea. It took place in Rome during the reign of Nero. A very cruel ruler who persecuted many Christians, Nero was known for taking believers and setting them on fire to light his garden at night. At that time a woman was captured and scheduled to be burned alive by Nero. Two of the younger Christians who had also been captured by Nero asked her, "Sister, we have heard all of our lives that God's grace is enough, but we are so young in the faith that we have never experienced it. We know that you have been scheduled to die. Tomorrow night, when you are set on fire, would you give us a signal if God's grace is really enough?"

> "The servant of God has a good master."
> —Randle Cotgrave

The woman told them that, if possible, she would give them a hand signal. She would raise her index finger in the air as a sign that God's grace was sufficient. Later that night, as Nero rode by, he lit them all on fire. As this woman's body went up in flames, she began to sing. As she did, she held up in the air not one finger, but two, and sang, "more than enough…more than enough. God's grace is more than enough."[1]

Reflect and Respond …

Think about and jot down how confident of God's grace you are as you lead on campus.

Are you willing to trust God for more than enough? Write a prayer expressing your heart's desire for His grace while you are a student.

Assess Yourself

In the space below list the differences between performance and service. If you need help remembering all twelve, you can refer to page 13, but do as much as you can from memory.

PERFORMANCE   **SERVICE**

As a leader, what place is service going to take in your ministry?

Guided Prayer
Father,
You know my heart,
and You know my
thoughts. You, Lord,
know the motivation
behind my service.
Protect me from the
performance trap.

Let my leadership be
an offering to You,
and my servanthood
a picture of You
in my life.

Fill my life with Your
grace, as You work in
both my life and
heart. Let everything
that I do be to Your
praise, glory, and
honor.

I love You, Father.

Amen.

How will you avoid the performance trap? What steps will you take to ensure success in your life?

Application

As a Christian leader on campus, if you have noticed yourself falling into the performance trap mentioned in this lesson, the best solution is to sit down and pray for the Lord to change your heart. Go through the seven steps on the previous page again. It might help to print the list and place it somewhere where you'll notice it frequently. Don't waste any time. Serve with all your heart and find the joy in doing it out of love for God, the One who has already done far more than we could ever return.

Priorities of a Leader

HOW YOU CAN MAKE THE MOST OF YOUR TIME

"Teach us to number our days aright, that we may gain a heart of wisdom."
—Psalm 90:12

"Woe to you, teachers of the law and Pharisees, you hypocrites! You give a tenth of your spices ... But you have neglected the more important matters of the law—justice, mercy and faithfulness. You should have practiced the latter, without neglecting the former. You blind guides! You strain out a gnat but swallow a camel."
—Matthew 23:23-24

During the 1990s, the space programs of the United States and Russian performed some joint ventures—projects never before attempted by either country.

NASA sent up female astronaut Shannon Lucid to represent the U.S. She joined Russian cosmonauts on the space station Mir. While they were there, the cosmonauts were scheduled to do some exploration away from the rest of the unit. In a humorous fashion, they communicated their expectations to Shannon, who would remain on board to watch after the equipment. In essence, they said to her: "Now you are in charge, but don't touch anything."

Many times we as leaders feel as though we are victims. We are in charge but not in control. We are responsible—but we feel we don't have a handle on what we must do to accomplish our goals.

Andy was a junior at the university he attended. That year, he was an R.A. in the dorm, led a ministry team every Wednesday night, was dating someone he felt might just be the girl he would marry, and was in charge of a homecoming event in the spring. He felt paralyzed. No doubt, he said, "yes" to too many things, but he didn't feel right about flaking out on his commitments. Now he didn't know what to do first.

Often leaders have only enough time to respond to immediate needs because we do not know the difference between the important and the immediate. We play defense with our calendars rather than offense. We run our schedules by default. *One of the first rules a leader must master is to "boss" the calendar and the resources of the team.* It has been said that leaders can do anything, but cannot do everything. Priorities are one of the most strategic issues you will face: What activities will consume your time? What people will you invest in? What projects will receive your best effort? Making right decisions about these issues requires you to understand the "Pareto Principle." Before we examine this principle, consider these questions.

Reflect and Respond ...

As a student, do you have enough time in your day? Why or why not?

Do you feel you are a slave to the tyranny of the urgent on campus? How?

The Principle

The "Pareto Principle" teaches us that if we focus our attention on our most important activities, we gain the highest return on our effort. In fact, Mr. Pareto found that if we tend to the top 20 percent most important priorities, we will accomplish 80 percent of the results we desire. Some call this the 80/20 Rule. The principle can be applied to your everyday life and enable you to lead more effectively.

Take a look at the diagram below. The column on the left represents your "to do" list. Getting done your first and second priorities will give you back 80 percent of your desired results. This occurs because many of the lower priorities are minor tasks that need to be completed (sometimes urgently), but are not extremely important. They are not the priorities you should focus on. If you embrace the right priorities, the vital activities that only you can do, then 20 percent of your effort will gain you 80 percent of the results and fruit you are shooting for.[1]

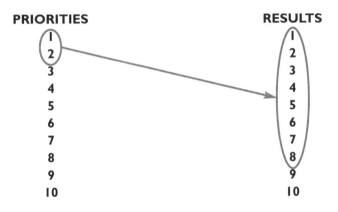

Examples of the Principle

Time:	20 percent of your time produces 80 percent of the results
People:	20 percent of the people do 80 percent of the work
Leadership:	20 percent of the people make 80 percent of the decisions
Growth:	20 percent of the members bring 80 percent of the new people
Programs:	20 percent of the activities give 80 percent of the growth
Finances:	20 percent of the people give 80 percent of the money
Reading:	20 percent of the book gives you 80 percent of the content
Sermons:	20 percent of the messages provide 80 percent of the impact

What Would Jesus Do?

Many times when we finish priorities 3-10, we feel as though we are being effective because we've been so busy! In reality, little is being done compared to the greater good that could be accomplished by tending to priorities 1 and 2. We're active, but not productive.

Take a look at Jesus in Mark 1:32-38. The text says that the whole city had gathered to see Him. Jesus was healing, casting out demons, and genuinely helping people. Then suddenly (with some of their needs still unmet) He left for a solitary place. Peter hunted Him down and said, "Everyone is looking for You." In other words, "Hey, You didn't finish helping everyone, and they're still back at my home!" Jesus replied, "Let us go somewhere else to the towns nearby, in order that I may preach there also; for that is what I came out for."

This statement doesn't make sense unless you understand the issue of priorities. Instead of receiving His mandate from Peter and the cries of the people, Jesus retreated to a solitary place to listen to His Heavenly Father. After recapturing His perspective, and refocusing on big-picture priorities, He shocked Peter by saying essentially: "I recognize everyone is looking for Me back at your house, but I've just spent time adjusting My priorities with My Father, and He says that it is time to move on."

Not only is Jesus a marvelous Savior, He is a model of a leader on a mission. He possessed definite priorities, based on a clear mission. He didn't treat everyone fairly by their standards. He invested far more time into twelve men than in the masses. In fact, He didn't even spend equal time with all of His twelve disciples. Three of them—Peter, James, and John— experienced exclusive ministry engagements with Him. Why? Because He was preparing them for crucial roles in the church later. He planned His work, and worked His plan.

Respond and Reflect ...

At first glance, it appears that Jesus only reacted to peoples' needs in the Gospels. List some examples from His life that let you know He had a set plan and definite priorities for His day. For example, the first one might be that "He performed miracles." Now you fill in the rest.

What determines the items that fill your daily calendar on a regular school day?

Do you find yourself reacting more to the clamoring of urgent needs or to the voice of God? Who determines your priorities on campus?

Group Up
Discuss how these 12 items could change your present campus leadership situation related to time.

How Can I Get More Out of My Day?

How do you spend your time? Can you get more out of your day? Test yourself and see. The following quiz will give you a good understanding of how well you manage your time. This quiz is based on the concepts of Jimmy Calano and Jeff Salzman, founders of "Career Track," a leading national training organization. Try it and see where you stand.

1. Do you plan tomorrow's work today?	Yes	No
2. Have you learned to perform routine chores at your daily "low" ebb and creative tasks at your "high" peak?	Yes	No
3. Do you get unpleasant duties out of the way as soon as possible?	Yes	No
4. Have you tried a "preview review": running the day through your head on the way to work?	Yes	No
5. Are you able to deal bluntly with people who waste your time?	Yes	No
6. Do you know how to log your time—that is, occasionally write down just how long it takes to accomplish each day's tasks?	Yes	No
7. When you promise that you'll get something done on time, do you always try to keep your word?	Yes	No
8. Do you set aside a portion of each day to think, create, and plan?	Yes	No
9. Is your desk or other workplace tidy? Can you find what you need without wasting time?	Yes	No
10. Do you have an efficient filing or equipment-organization system?	Yes	No
11. Do you know how to choose your most productive tasks?	Yes	No
12. Do you know exactly what your top priorities are?	Yes	No

Evaluate Your Score

If you responded yes to 10-12 questions above, you handle your time excellently.

If you responded yes to 7-9 questions above, you are good, but still need to grow.

If you responded yes to 6 or less, you are wasting valuable time and may not even know it.

Reflect and Respond ...

How did you do on the test? Write down the areas you see that can be improved in your day.

Time is more valuable than money. You can get more money, but you can't get more time.

Getting Rid of the Non-Essentials

In Jules Verne's novel *The Mysterious Island,* he tells of five men who escaped a civil war prison by hijacking a hot-air balloon. As they rose into the air, they realized the wind was taking them over the ocean, and they wondered how much longer the balloon would stay afloat. As the hours passed and the surface of the ocean drew closer, the men decided they must cast overboard some of the weight because they had no way to heat the air in the balloon. Shoes, overcoats, weapons, and other things were reluctantly discarded. The men were uncomfortable, but the balloon rose temporarily. Soon they found themselves very close to the waves again, so they tossed their food. Better to be high and hungry than to drown on a full belly! Unfortunately, this too was temporary, and the craft again threatened to lower the men into the sea. One man had an idea: they could tie the ropes that hold the passenger car and sit on those ropes. Then they could cut away the basket beneath them. As they severed the very thing that they had been sitting on, it dropped into the ocean, and the balloon rose. Not a minute too soon they spotted land. Eager to again be on the ground, the five jumped into the water and swam to the island. They lived, spared because they were able to discern the difference between what was really needed and what was not. The "necessities" they once thought they couldn't live without were the very weights that almost cost them their lives.[2]

The same can happen to us in our everyday lives as students. We too need to be able to distinguish the difference between what is necessary and what is expendable.

Lessons We Can Learn from the 80/20 Principle

1. It is not how hard we work, but how smart we work.
Working smarter means working on what we can do, and delegating things others can do. What good is it to work extremely hard when it accomplishes little?

2. We either organize or we agonize.
If we can learn to organize, we can become more efficient in getting things done. This in turn will save us a lot of time and frustration. Have you discovered this in your student life?

3. We choose or we lose. If we don't evaluate, we will stagnate.
Looking at where we stand is very important. To move to the next level of leadership we must evaluate our current situation.

4. The issue is not: will my calendar be full, but what will fill my calendar?
Success in planning is about scheduling our priorities, not prioritizing our schedules. Like the men on the balloon, anything that is not essential must be discarded.

5. Will our days be filled by our priorities or by the requests of others?
As leaders, there are certain things we can do that others cannot. When we fill our days with completing the requests of others, we will not be able to get done the tasks that only we can do. As a Christian student, does God have priorities for your life?

6. Will we lead or will we react?
When we lose control, we are no longer acting as leaders, but instead reacting to the immediate. When we are determined to lead, reacting is not good enough. We need to be proactive and lead.

"Let us throw off everything that hinders and the sin that so easily entangles" (Heb. 12:1).

Group Up
Talk about what needs to be thrown out of your life now as a student.

How will you do it?

A Lesson from the Rocks

A while back I attended a seminar on the subject of time management. That day an expert was speaking to a group of students and said, "OK, it is time for a quiz." Then he pulled out a one-gallon, wide-mouthed jar and set it on a table in front of him. He then produced about a dozen fist-sized rocks and carefully placed them one at a time into the jar. When the jar was filled to the top and no more rocks would fit inside, he asked, "Is the jar full?" Everyone in the class said, "Yes." Then he said, "Really?" He reached under the table and pulled out a bucket of gravel. Then he dumped some gravel in and shook the jar, causing pieces of the gravel to work themselves down into the spaces between the big rocks. Then he asked the group once more, "Is the jar full?" By this time the class was on to him. "Probably not," one of the students answered. "Good," he replied. He reached under the table and brought out a bucket of sand. He started dumping the sand in and it went into all the spaces left between the rocks and the gravel. "Is the jar full?" he again asked. "No!" the class shouted. Then he grabbed a pitcher of water and began to pour it in until the jar was filled to the brim. Then the speaker said to his class, "The truth here is that you must put the big rocks in first."

The same is true with our lives. When we fill our lives first with many trivial things, we often find that we will not have room for the few things that are most important. As a college student, remember, it's not about prioritizing your schedule, but scheduling your priorities.

Reflect and Respond ...

Below are four fundamental questions to help you to get control of your calendar. Write your answer below each question and see if they can give you a better perspective on what is most important.

List three things that are the most important to you as a student.

How much time will each one take?

What are my deadlines?

When can I make each of them?

How to Determine Priorities

In finding your priorities, it is just as important to look at what is not directly fulfilling your mission as what is. *Remember, focus is about discarding any and all things that are holding you back from being as effective as possible.* Following are the three R's. They will help you start to find where your focus should be. Ask yourself these three questions and see if they help you.

1. Requirement: What is required of me?
When you feel overwhelmed by obligations, stop to sort out your "must-dos" from your "choose-to-dos." Our obligations in life are the biggest priorities we have; but more often than not, you will find that you really do not have to do many things, you choose to do them. Simply ask: *What must I do? What is required of me here?*[3]

At age 19, I became a pastor. I didn't feel ready for the job, but I was excited about ministering to high school students in a youth group. Soon I was given other tasks, projects, and ministries to do in the church. I was forced to separate my "must-do's" from my "choose-to- do's." My being willing to make those tough choices served my ministry and maintained my personal sanity! The key to this was completing the "must-do's," the things that were most important.

Often the little things in life can trip us up. A tragic example of this is the 1972 Eastern Airlines jumbo jet crash in the Florida Everglades. The plane was the now famous Flight 401, bound from New York to Miami with a heavy load of holiday passengers.

As the plane approached the Miami airport for landing, the control light that indicates proper deployment of the landing gear failed to go on. The plane flew in a large, looping circle over the swamps of the Everglades while the cockpit crew checked to see if the gear actually had not deployed, or if instead the bulb in the control light was defective. When the flight engineer tried to remove the light bulb, it would not budge, and the other members of the crew tried to help him. As they struggled with the bulb, no one noticed the aircraft was losing altitude, and the plane simply flew right into the swamp. Dozens of people were killed in the crash.

While experienced pilots fiddled with a seventy-five-cent bulb, the plane flew into the ground.

2. Results: What gives the greatest return?
When sorting out priorities, ask the question: *what gives me the greatest results when I do it?* As a student, you should spend most of your time working in the area of your greatest strength. He is a wise man who wastes no energy on pursuits for which he is not fitted; and he is wiser still who from among the things he can do well, chooses and follows the best. Find your gift and capitalize your time using it. Begin to think as a student, what are the results that you want to see in your life? How will you get those results?[4]

Looking for the right results reminds me of a story about an amazing 1906 football season of St. Louis University. Until that time, the game of football was a low-scoring, slow-running game. In 1906 the forward pass was legalized. However, in 1906 everyone ignored this new rule. They were satisfied with the results they had achieved thus far; everyone, that is, except St. Louis University. The coaches there quickly saw the benefit of this new change and switched their old offense to a new offense that used the forward pass. The result was that they outscored their opponents 402-11 that season. This happened because the coaches were willing to look for what would give them the greatest return. Like St. Louis University, choosing to change in order to get the greatest return is a risk. You step out of the known and into possibilities; you step out of tradition and into innovation. In the end, it all boils down to stepping out of your comfort zone, and choosing to find the greatest return. Remember, many times the chief enemy of the "Best" is the "Good."[5]

"If you forget the ultimate, you will become a slave to the immediate."
—unknown

3. Reward: What gives me the greatest joy?

Finally, as you sort through personal priorities, look for the element of personal fulfillment. God provides deep satisfaction when you do what He has gifted and called you to do. There is nothing easier than not finding time to do the things you don't want to do. Do you find greater rewards in some things that you do instead of others?[6]

When Apple Computers fell on difficult days a while back, Apple's young chairman, Steve Jobs, traveled from the Silicon Valley to New York City. His purpose was to convince Pepsico's John Sculley to move west and run his struggling company. As the two men overlooked the Manhattan skyline from Sculley's penthouse office, the Pepsi executive started to decline Jobs's offer. "Financially," Sculley said, "you'd have to give me a million-dollar salary, a million-dollar bonus, and a million-dollar severance."

Flabbergasted, Jobs gulped and agreed—if Sculley would move to California. But Sculley would commit only to being a consultant from New York. At that Jobs issued a challenge to Sculley. "Do you want to spend the rest of your life selling sugared water, or do you want to change the world?"

In his autobiography, *Odyssey,* Sculley admits Jobs's challenge "knocked the wind out of me." He said that he had become so caught up with his future at Pepsi, high pension, and whether or not his family could adapt to life in California that an opportunity to "change the world" nearly passed him by. Instead, he put his life in perspective and went to Apple.[7]

Many students don't recognize the chance to change the world. Your greatest fulfillment lies in using your gifts in a cause that counts for eternity.

> "Try not to become a man of success, but rather try to become a man of value."
> —Albert Einstein

Reflect and Respond ...

What are some non-essentials in your life? List several here.

What gives you the greatest return when you do it?

In what activities do you find joy?

Application: Write Down Your Top 20 Percent

Now that we have reviewed the principle, take a moment to think about your application to the principle. Remember: activity does not equal accomplishment. Answer the following questions based on your own leadership strengths and priorities:

1. Who are the top 20 percent influential people you should pour your life into?

_____   _____

_____   _____

_____   _____

2. What activities result in the greatest amount of fruit for you as a leader?

_____   _____
_____   _____
_____   _____

3. Who are the potential leaders around you who you can equip for ministry or leadership?

_____   _____
_____   _____
_____   _____

4. When you lead, what gives you the deepest sense of fulfillment?

_____   _____
_____   _____
_____   _____

5. List other priorities you should pursue, as you endeavor to lead other students.

_____   _____
_____   _____
_____   _____

Priorities vs. Distractions

In order to establish what is most important, college leaders must gain perspective. A former police officer provides a great analogy. He tells of the tactics of roving bands of thieves who used to rob convenient stores:

They enter the store as a group. One or two separate themselves from the group, and the others start a loud commotion in another section of the store. This commotion grabs the attention of the clerks and customers. As all eyes are turned to the disturbance, the accomplices fill their pockets with merchandise and cash, leaving before anyone suspects.

Hours—sometimes even days later—the victimized merchant realizes things are missing and calls the police. Too late. How often the Evil One uses this strategy. We are seduced into paying attention to the distractions, and miss what we should be focusing on.

Priorities usually come into focus when we go through a crisis. During tragedy, we tend to forget the petty distractions and focus on what counts. For instance, do you remember the terrorist attacks on the World Trade Center and the Pentagon? Of course, you do. It all happened Tuesday, September 11, 2001. The day before, most of us were distracted with petty things. What a difference that one day made.

On Monday—people were fighting about prayer in public schools.
On Tuesday—you would have been hard pressed to find a school that wasn't praying.

On Monday—people were trying to separate each other by race, sex, skin color, ...
On Tuesday—nearly everyone was holding hands, working together, crying together.

On Monday—people were talking about heroes as being athletes.
On Tuesday—people looked at firefighters or EMS workers to learn what _hero_ meant.

On Monday—people were fighting over the Ten Commandments on government land.
On Tuesday—people all said, "God help us" while thinking: Thou shalt not kill.

"There is no security in this life, only opportunity."
—Douglas MacArthur

On Monday—students went to class with no sense of meaning.
On Tuesday—students went to class with a new sense of meaning and purpose.

On Monday—people were upset that traffic moved so slowly.
On Tuesday—people stood in long lines to give blood.

On Monday—politicians argued about budget surpluses.
On Tuesday—grief stricken, they joined together and sang "God Bless America."

On Monday—students were irritated that their homework was too great.
On Tuesday—students gave generously to the Red Cross and Salvation Army.

It's all about perspective. Let me take it one step further. Most questions of priority are not between something important and something trivial—but rather between the important and the most important.

Where Does My Time Go?

In a lifetime (70 years) we spend...

21 years sleeping
6 years traveling
1 year looking for lost items
14 years working
7 years in the bathroom
6 years eating
5 years waiting in line
3 years in meetings
2 years returning calls
22 months in worship
8 months opening junk mail
6 months waiting on red lights

Checklist for Making Decisions

Try using these five questions when making decisions in your role as a leader on campus. Let them act as a screen in planning your priorities on campus and throughout the day.

1. Is this consistent with my priorities?
2. Is this within my area of competence?
3. Can someone else do it better?
4. What do my trusted friends say?
5. Do I have the time?

Group Up
How easy is it for you to say no? Can you manage the requests of others in your schedule? Discuss it in your group.

How to Say No Gracefully

Many times, the problem that we have is not that we have too much to do, but more so that other people have too much they think we can/should do. In times like this, when the task would not further your goal, you need to learn to just say no. *How* you say no is many times as important as *when* you say it.

1. Say no to the proposition—not to the person.

Be sure the person understands that you are not rejecting them; what they want you to do is something you won't do. Try giving them an affirmation about what they are doing and gently add that it just doesn't fit in with the things that you need to accomplish.

2. Respond in terms of the best interest of the person asking.

Be sure the person knows that you're not just blowing them off, but that you want to genuinely help them when your priorities will permit. Communicate that your time constraints would actually prevent you from doing the kind of work they deserve.

3. Defer creatively. Come up with an alternative.

Think of some way that would help them complete their task. Give them confidence that they can do it, or maybe help them find someone who will. This affirmation will aid them in solving their problem.

Making the Most of Your Time

1. Make a "to do" list.

Write out what you want to accomplish on campus and other places today.

2. Set your priorities.

After you make a list, find the most important things and put them at the top of the list.

3. Avoid perfectionism.

Don't aim to do something perfect, if it ties up so much time that it paralyzes you from progress. Do things with excellence; perfectionism may be an extreme that you need to avoid.

4. Question everything.

Don't allow any "sacred cows" (such as thinking you must always spend 10 hours a day in the library) to keep you from eliminating items from your calendar and "to do" lists. If it doesn't work, get rid of it.

5. Welcome tension.

Stressing out about something doesn't get you any closer to completing your goal. Understand that tension is a part of life. Many times tension can actually improve your focus and enable you to complete the job more effectively.

6. Avoid clutter.

Clutter will just get in the way of what you are doing. Try not to waste time searching for things. After all, your dorm room can't be that big. It has to be there somewhere.

7. Avoid procrastination.

Don't just do what is fun first (major temptation); get what needs to be done first, done first.

8. Control interruptions and distractions.

Minimize the amount of time that other students take away from your main objective.

9. Learn to read faster and selectively.

Reading quickly as well as understanding what essentially needs to be read will give you more time in accomplishing your goal. Sure, it's a big textbook. Learn what needs to be read.

10. Use a calendar.

Organizing your days will save time, and help to organize your priorities.

"The last thing one knows is what to put first."
—Pascal

Are these ten things doable in making the most of the time in your life? List some areas that need improvement.

Go back to the ten and draw a star next to the top three skills that you need to work on the most. Make a goal to improve them. For clarity, you may want to list your three here.

One Thousand Marbles

I love the story of the 1000 marbles. Listen to the story of one man's account and determine if your time can be improved by just a few marbles.

"The older I get, the more I enjoy Saturday mornings. Perhaps it's the quiet solitude that comes with being the first to rise, or maybe the unbounded joy of not having to be at work.

"A few weeks ago, I was shuffling toward the basement shack with a steaming cup of coffee in one hand and the morning paper in the other. What began as a typical Saturday morning, turned into one of those lessons that life seems to hand you from time to time.

"I turned the dial up on the phone portion of the band on my ham radio in order to listen to a Saturday morning swap meet. Along the way, I came across an older sounding chap, with a tremendous signal and a golden voice. You know the kind—he sounded like he should be in the broadcasting business. He was telling whoever he was talking with something about 'a thousand marbles.'

"I was intrigued and stopped to listen to what he had to say. 'Well, Tom, it sure sounds like you're busy with your job. I'm sure they pay you well, but it is a shame that you have to be away from home and your family so much. Hard to believe that a young fellow should have to work 60 or 70 hours to make ends meet. Too bad you missed your daughter's dance recital.'

"He continued, 'Let me tell you something, Tom—something that has helped me keep a good perspective on my own priorities.' And that's when he started to explain his theory of 'a thousand marbles.' 'You see, I sat down one day and did a little arithmetic. The average person lives about 75 years. I know some live more and some live less, but on average, folks live about 75 years.'

"'Now then, I multiplied 75 times 52 and I came up with 3900, which is the number of Saturdays that the average person has in their entire lifetime. Now, stick with me, Tom. I am getting to the important part.'

"'It took me until I was 55-years-old to think about all this in any detail', he went on. 'And by that time, I have lived through over 2800 Saturdays. I got to thinking that if I lived to be 75, I had only about 1000 of them left to enjoy.'

"'So I went to a toy store and bought every single marble that they had. I ended up having to visit three toy stores to round up 1000 marbles. I took them home and put them inside a large, clear plastic container right here in the shack next to my gear. Every Saturday since then, I have taken one marble out and thrown it away.'

"'I found that by watching the marbles diminish, I focused more on the really important things in life. There is nothing like watching your time here on earth run out to help you get priorities straight.'

"'Now, let me tell you one last thing before I sign-off with you and take my lovely wife out to breakfast. This morning, I took the very last marble out of the container. I figure if I make it until next Saturday, then I have been given a little extra time. And the one thing we all can use is a little more time.'

"'It was nice to meet you, Tom. I hope you spend more time with your family, and I hope to meet you again on the band. 73 Old Man, this is K9NZQ clear and going QRT, good morning!'

"You could have head a pin drop on the band when this fellow signed off. I guess he gave us a lot to think about. I had planned to work on the antenna that morning, and then I was going to meet up with a few hams to work on the next club newsletter. Instead, I went upstairs and woke up my wife with a kiss. 'C'mon, honey, I am taking you and the kids out to breakfast.'

"'What brought this on?' she asked with a smile. 'Oh, nothing special. It's just been a long time since we spent a Saturday together with the kids. Hey, can we stop at a toy store while we're out? I need to buy some marbles.'"

Reflect and Respond ...

Why is it important for collegiate leaders to know and focus on the right priorities? Jot down three or four ideas you may have related to the issue of time and priorities.

Father,
I know that finding my priorities is important if I ever want to accomplish the mission You have for me.

Give me wisdom to see all the things that may be getting in my way, and the strength to cut these things out of my life that are hindering me from reaching the ultimate goal.

Reveal Your plan to me, and show me how I may be of service right now.

Thank You for Your faithfulness and guidance.

Amen.

Assess Yourself

As a student, do you have control of your time?   ❏ Yes   ❏ No   ❏ Sometimes
How do you think you can do a better job of managing your priorities?

As a leader on your campus, do your priorities take the primary role in your life? If not, be as honest as you can and write down what takes your time, then next to it write down what should take your time. Take a minute and review your answers. Cross out the ones of least importance.

Application

What one step will you take this week toward practicing the Pareto Principle? Use this space to clarify and write down your one step.

With the list of things you have made throughout the chapter, make a compilation of all those ideas in the extra space on this page. If you like, you can use a separate piece of paper. Start with things like: *What are my main priorities?* (How to determine priorities) *What are the non-essentials in my life?* (What would Jesus do?) *How can I get more time out of my day?* (Time quiz).

Teamwork Makes the Dream Work

RECRUITING AND RELEASING TEAM PLAYERS

*"A body isn't really a body, unless there is more than one part.
It takes many parts to make a single body."*
—1 Corinthians 12:19-20

*"Two people can accomplish more than twice as much as one;
they get a better return for their labor."*
—Ecclesiastes 4:9 (NLT)

Need a Hand?

When lightning struck Wayne Burkholder's barn near Farmerstown, Ohio, it burned down in a hurry. When 700 men in his Amish community showed up two weeks later to help him build his new barn, it went up in a hurry, too. The men began arriving in their Amish buggies right after breakfast, and the roof was on the barn when they broke for lunch. Everyone played a role. Some from the community handled the roofing, some the raising of the walls, some the painting, and some handed out the lemonade and made lunch. What nature ruined in less than six hours, teamwork was able to restore in less than six hours!

How foreign this approach may sound to the independent mindset we have in America. Yet God did not cut any of us out for the kind of things that we often celebrate: the maverick spirit, the renegade, the individual, the lone ranger. Even though we've adopted a "do-it-on-your-own" mentality, ministry was never intended to be done alone. As we discussed in the first chapter, all good leaders are driven by vision—by a dream. This is true for the collegiate leader. But every leader will need a hand in making that dream a reality. God did not design leadership in the body of Christ to take place in a vacuum, isolated and alone. In order to make the dream work, you need teamwork. Jesus selected a team of twelve. Paul traveled with a team of workers made up of Luke, Timothy, Barnabas, Silas, Mark, Demas, and others. In the Old Testament, Moses had his team of elders, David had his mighty men, and Elijah had his school of prophets. Ministry was designed to take place in teams. The amazing thing is that as we approach our dreams, think of all on campus who are helping to make them a reality. We're to do it together.

Imagine how long it would have taken Wayne Burkholder to resurrect his barn if he had been left to do it on his own. Think how confusing it would have been if everyone came together, but each person wanted to do their own thing, instead of cooperating. Without a team working together to help rebuild his barn, the Burkholder barn might still be in ruins. And not only does teamwork get the job done more effectively and efficiently, a community is formed on the way. As a college student, you will find meaning in being part of a team, not just by arriving at the goal. We all need to be part of something bigger than ourselves and we need the relationships that are formed in the process. Simply put, we all need the components of teamwork:[1]

Basic Truth

One is too small of a number to accomplish anything great. God calls leaders to coach teams.

Guided Prayer

Father,
As we lead on campus, help us to understand the importance of our team.
Help us not to have a lone-wolf mentality, but instead to embrace our brothers and sisters in love. Lord, we know that we are just a piece of the puzzle; we are one part in the whole body of Christ. Give us a better understanding of these things, and prepare our minds for this lesson.
We thank You in advance for what You will accomplish.

Amen.

What characteristic of teamwork that is designed to help you reach a goal do you find attractive as a Christian on campus? Discuss it in your group.

I need a **CAUSE** that is bigger than me.
I need a **COMMUNITY** that provides supportive relationships.
I need to make a **CONTRIBUTION** based on my specific God-given gifts.

Building a Winning Team

Have you ever stopped to consider that one is too small of a number to accomplish anything great? When you think about great movements throughout history, God usually used teams of people working together to change the world. God may start with one person, but a team is generally recruited to reach the goal. That is how Moses led the people of Israel in the wilderness (Ex. 18). That is how Nehemiah built the Jerusalem wall (Neh. 2-3). That is how Jesus spread the word about the kingdom of God during His earthly ministry (Matt. 10). God usually doesn't call "lone rangers"; He calls members of the body of Christ. The word *saint* appears only once in the New Testament. The word *saints* (in the plural form) appears dozens of times. God wants us to work together!

Reflect and Respond ...

Think of some ways you have experienced teamwork in your past. If you can, list two or three things that made the team work.

Great Teams Possess ...

For your team to work, it must possess three important ingredients:

1. A common goal and vision. Each team rallies around a single goal and vision. The entire team understands the vision and buys into it. They are all running in the same direction with their eyes on the same end result. Have you and other students had this experience?

2. Diverse skills and contribution. A good collegiate team is made up of a group of people who compliment each other. Your team may or may not be just other students. The members of the team are not all alike. Imagine a baseball team made up of only shortstops. The team wouldn't do so well, would it? A team requires students with a variety of skills contributing in different areas.

3. Strong coaching and communication. Every collegiate team needs to have someone providing vision and giving direction. Great teams have coaches who are purposeful. Further, both the coaches and players are constantly communicating and giving feedback to each other as they work. If you haven't done so, find a team to help you do better with your studies.

"There are no problems that we cannot solve together, and very few that we can solve by ourselves."
—Lyndon Johnson

Pictures of Christian Teamwork in the Bible

Scripture provides us with many portraits of people working as a team: many people working together as though they were one person! This is why we're called the BODY of Christ. We are many parts, but work together toward one ultimate goal and function.

Picture 1: The Four Men and Their Paralyzed Friend

(Luke 5:17-26)
In this story, the four men who carried their paralyzed friend to Jesus encountered obstacles. Fortunately, that didn't stop them from reaching their goal. Their eyes were set on one thing and one thing only: getting their friend to Jesus. They eventually cut a hole in the roof and let the paralytic down through the hole in order for him to be placed right in front of his healer.

The Gospels contain stories of 40 people who were healed by Jesus. Thirty-four of those 40 people were brought to Jesus by someone else, such as the paralytic in this story. The Bible is a story of teamwork: people helping people find God. It is a team of people working toward a common goal!

Group Up
What makes the dynamic of teamwork so difficult?

Picture 2: Nehemiah and His Team of Builders

Nehemiah 3-4
Nehemiah knew that a broken wall was a disgrace to God, but he also knew he couldn't build it alone. He had to recruit a team of men to rebuild the wall around Jerusalem. If you read Nehemiah 3-4, you will see the number it took to accomplish such a task. Listed is name after name of families who undertook different tasks to rebuild various parts of the wall. Some men laid bricks and others acted as guards to protect the builders from their enemies who tried to thwart their efforts.

Not only did they rebuild it, but that team got the "impossible" task done in 52 days! It took each person in the story contributing something different. Each worked on a separate part of the wall, like players on a football team. It was a team of people with diverse skills and contributions!

Picture 3: Paul and the Shipwreck

Acts 27
To paraphrase Acts 27, Paul was taken prisoner and found himself on a ship heading toward Rome to appear before Caesar. Along the journey they encountered a terrible storm and were shipwrecked. Despite being a prisoner, Paul stepped forward as the "coach" who guided the passengers to safety.

"No one had eaten for a long time. Finally, Paul called the crew together and said, 'Men, you should have listened to me in the first place and not left Fair Havens. You would have avoided all this injury and loss. But take courage! None of you will lose your life, even though the ship will go down. For last night an angel of the God to whom I belong and whom I serve stood beside me, and he said, 'Don't be afraid, Paul, for you will surely stand trial before Caesar! What's more, God in His goodness has granted safety to everyone sailing with you' " (author's paraphrase).

Paul, an inmate, became the chief influencer on the ship during the storm. He provided clear direction to everyone, and gave them confidence that they would reach their goal. It was a team of people with strong coaching and communication!

Reflect and Respond ...

Have you had experiences on your team similar to the previous three? If not, think of ways you can build them into your team. List two or three ideas in the margin for future reference.

Recruiting Your Own Team

Now that we've done an overview of what is necessary to make a good team, it's time to dig deeper. Let's begin by examining how you can recruit the right team members for your team.

Have you considered exactly what you want to accomplish with your team? The kind of students and other people you recruit should be determined by the goals you believe God has given you. The members are gifts to the team. The key is GIFTS. Consider this little grid as you seek students to join your team. If you spot all five in someone—go get 'em!

G — GIFTED MEMBERS
Look for specific gifts and abilities in other students that are crucial to achieve your goals.

I — INFLUENTIAL PEOPLE
Look for students who have influence with others. You may want to consider someone in a fraternity or sorority for your team.

F — FAITHFUL WORKERS
Look for students who are already faithful to Christian commitments they have made.

T — TEACHABLE SPIRIT
Look for students who are willing to learn and be flexible with teammates.

S — SERVANT'S HEART
Look for fellow students who want to serve others, not gain recognition.

How to Ask Them

When you have located students you think would be great team members, follow these steps as you challenge those persons to join up:

1. Meet with them and get acquainted with their goals. Be sure they want to head in the same direction you do.

2. Take time to share your vision with them. Don't detail the tasks before you give them a clear, big-picture perspective of your dream. Share your passion.

3. Ask where they believe they might fit into the vision being given to them. Let them respond and participate in discussing the big idea with you.

4. Allow them to think and pray about it. Don't pressure them for an immediate answer.

5. Schedule a time to meet again to discuss questions and next steps.

Group Up
Have you seen relationships deteriorate on a team on campus? How about in your church? In your opinion, what was the cause? What was the result? Discuss it in your group.

What Makes an Effective Team?

Now for the big question. What is necessary in a Christian team for it to accomplish its goal? When you reduce it to the fundamentals, there are ten main components that make a team effective. As we work our way through these, evaluate the campus team you are currently on or a team that you have been a part of in the past to determine how effective you really are.

1. An effective team cares for one another.

Think about it: what motivates you to be a team player? What pushes you to give 110 percent to your team? Is it because you feel a sense of duty or obligation? Is it a sense of "have to" that provides the incentive? Usually not. Although this may carry you so far, motivation generally comes from the relationships you form with your team members. The foundation of any successful team is relationship. Without feeling cared for, the members will soon check out. Three principles help explain why relationship is so essential for the success of a team.

Three Principles of Relationships a Leader Needs to Know

• **The Second-Mile Principle**—People go the "first mile" because of a sense of duty. They go the "second mile" because of relationship.

• **The Connection Principle**—Leaders always touch a heart before they ask for a hand. If you connect relationally, people will gladly join you in the work.

• **The Host Principle**—Good leaders always "host" the conversation and relationships of their lives. They initiate rather than wait for others to serve them.

Shoulder to Shoulder

Jackie Robinson was the first African American to play in the major leagues. He played his first game for the Brooklyn Dodgers in April, 1947. Although he had the talent to play in the major leagues, the first month was tough for him. Many of his own teammates did not want him on the team. There was a petition passed around the team declaring they did not want to play with a black man. Even in Brooklyn, he was jeered and booed by the hometown fans. He couldn't eat meals at restaurants with the rest of the Dodgers or stay in the same hotels, just because he was black. Here he was, a major league player and he was alone. Reflecting back on that time, Jackie said he doesn't think he would have made it if it hadn't been for Pee Wee Reese.

Pee Wee Reese was the captain of the team. He approached Jackie soon after he joined the team, shook his hand, and apologized for the behavior of rest of the guys. From that time on, he took Jackie Robinson under his wing. It was not a moment too soon.

Jackie Robinson wrote later that the trip to Cincinnati to play the Reds was especially hard. Crosley field was a bellowing frenzy of booing, hissing, and yelling. One spectator even threw a black cat onto the field. They were hateful. Then it happened. A ground ball was hit to him. He reached down to field it and he bobbled the ball. He had lost his concentration. The fans went wild as they booed and screamed obscenities at him. Jackie just stood there with his head down, waiting for the next pitch. It was at that moment that Pee Wee Reese decided he had to do something.

Pee Wee ran up to the pitcher's mound to call a time-out. Then he walked over to Jackie. He put his arm around Jackie's shoulder and looked over the entire stadium until the crowd grew quiet. Jackie said later that the noise went down like someone had turned down a loud radio. Jackie said, "I think that arm around my shoulder saved my career."

"There is an old saying when it comes to teams: Either we are pulling together or we're pulling apart."

—John Maxwell

There are students near you right now for which an arm around their shoulder could make a difference. Effective teams care for one another, beyond the call of duty.

Evaluate yourself:
As a team, do we care for one another? Put a mark indicating where you are on the scale.

No_____Somewhat _____Yes
1   2   3   4   5   6   7   8   9   10

How can you ensure people feel cared for on your team?

2. An effective team knows and practices what's important.
An effective team is clear about its vision. It understands what it has been called together to do and knows its purpose. Everything the team does is in line with accomplishing that vision. No energy or time is wasted on things that don't contribute to the "big picture." On the other hand, an ineffective team is unclear in its purpose and therefore its priorities. The team may eventually accomplish its goal, but it may zigzag its way there, wasting time, energy, and resources along the way. Without clarity of vision—without knowing what is important—it is like the blind leading the way.

Who's Leading Who?

An elderly woman stood on a busy street corner, hesitant to cross because there was no traffic signal. As she waited, a gentleman came up beside her and asked, "May I cross over with you?" Relieved, she thanked him and took his arm.

The path they took was anything but safe. The man seemed to be confused as they dodged traffic and walked in a zigzag pattern across the street. "You almost got us killed!" the woman exclaimed in anger when they finally reached the curb. "You walk like you're blind!" "I am," he replied. "That's why I asked if I could cross with you."

Reflect and Respond ...

Do you know what is the vision of your campus team? State the team's vision in a sentence or two.

What are the top three priorities of a team you may be a part of?

1._____

2._____

3._____

Group Up
Does everyone on your team know his/her number-one priority?

Evaluate yourself:

As a team, do we know and act on what is important? Check one that applies.

❑ No ❑ Somewhat ❑ Yes ❑ Not sure

If you were rating your campus team on a scale of 1-10 with a 10 being the best, put a mark on this scale to indicate where you feel you are right now.

| 1 | 2 | 3 | 4 | 5 | 6 | 7 | 8 | 9 | 10 |

3. An effective team grows together.

Effective teams don't ever stay the same. Teams fall apart when they don't change and grow. As a Christian leader you must continue to improve so that you can continue to lead. If you stop growing today, you will stop leading tomorrow. Great teams are never satisfied with where they are. They are always pushing for growth and development; they invite change and take risks to stretch themselves. This should be indicative of your campus team.

There are several reasons why growth is important for a Christian team:
- The leader's growth determines the organization's growth. You cannot lead beyond where you have grown yourself. You should have a strong personal relationship with Christ.
- Life and the campus are constantly changing. If you are not addressing the changing needs of society, your work will be irrelevant.
- Leaders must improve to stay in front. If you are not improving, you will fall behind.
- Your leadership team must stay on the "same page." You need to be moving forward in the same direction. Remember Nehemiah?

All Yellow Stars

There is a story told from World War II when the Nazis invaded Denmark. Their plan was to exterminate the Jews in Denmark. The order from the Nazis was that all Jews should wear the Star of David so they could be identified. The king of Denmark was prepared, however. He decreed that all citizens of Denmark would wear a yellow Star of David so the Nazis couldn't tell Jews from Gentiles. The Danish people took a risk and did it. Jewish citizens wept the next day as they saw everyone wearing the Star of David. Because the Danes stood together, the Nazi plan was stymied. In a changing world, they adjusted and sacrificed to ensure the survival of the team.

Evaluate yourself:

As a team, are we growing together?

No_____Somewhat_____Yes
| 1 | 2 | 3 | 4 | 5 | 6 | 7 | 8 | 9 | 10 |

Based on what you have read, what can you do to grow as a Christian leader? Jot down two or three ideas.

> "There are no victories at bargain prices."
>
> —Dwight D. Eisenhower

Again, based on what you have read, what can be done to encourage growth on your team?

4. An effective team has a chemistry that fits.

Have you ever just "clicked" with someone? You meet a student, start a conversation with them, and find that you really connect. A similar chemistry occurs within a team when the right combination of people come together. There is a match, a fit that enables the team members to work in harmony with one another.

During the 1980s business leaders coined a term called *synergy*. It described the extra energy that surfaced when good chemistry and good talent came together. The results moved from addition to multiplication.

Here are some elements that contribute to the right "chemistry" occurring on a team...

• relationships are strong	• players are appreciated	• desires are similar
• morale is high	• trust is evident	• wins are frequent
• roles are clear	• motives are pure	• abilities are complimentary

Group Up
How can you tell if you have chemistry with another person in your campus group?

Play Harmony

CBS radio newsman Charles Osgood told the story of two ladies who lived in a convalescent center. Each had suffered an incapacitating stroke. Margaret's stroke had damaged her left side, while Ruth's stroke restricted her right side. Both of these ladies were accomplished pianists but had given up hope of ever playing again.

The director of the convalescent center, observing the frustration of these women, decided to try something. He asked them both to sit at a piano and encouraged them to play solo pieces—but together. As Margaret began playing with her good right hand and Ruth with her good left hand, a beautiful song emerged. What one was not able to do alone, two could do together—in harmony.[2]

Evaluate yourself:
As a team, do we have the right chemistry? Pick a spot and mark it on the scale below.

No_____Somewhat _____Yes
| 1 | 2 | 3 | 4 | 5 | 6 | 7 | 8 | 9 | 10 |

Look over the list of elements that contribute to the right chemistry. Think of how you can bolster these on your team. You may want to discuss this with other members of your team.

5. An effective team places an individual's rights below the team's best interest.
Being part of a Christian team is understanding that the whole, the team, is greater than its parts—the individuals. Cooperation is necessary for a team to succeed, which requires individual sacrifice. There must be a transition from an "I" mindset to a "we" mindset. When players are willing to take personal sacrifices for the sake of the team, the team tends to win.

Shave It or Ship Out

John Wooden was one of the greatest basketball coaches in NCAA history. As coach of the UCLA Bruins, he won more consecutive championships than anyone.

John led his team by values. He believed that the team was more important than any one player. He made sure that no player became a prima donna. No one had special rights. One rule he enforced, in fact, was that no player was allowed to have facial hair. More than once he was challenged on this rule when a great player would join the team wearing a mustache or beard.

When Bill Walton joined the squad as a freshman, he was already a star, out of Helix High School in La Mesa, California. Bill later went on to the NBA and led the Portland Trailblazers to a championship. He was a great player—but he had a beard. After hearing the rule about facial hair, he approached Coach Wooden and said, "I'm gonna keep my beard, Coach." Walton expected special treatment because of his talent. He assumed he would be an exception. But team values were more important to Wooden. The coach just smiled and said, "We're going to miss you, Bill."[3]

Needless to say, Bill shaved his beard, the team became more important to him than his own rights—and they went on to win a championship.

The Code of Cooperation

- carry your load
- respect other team members
- understand others' value
- look for ways to add value to others
- come together ready to contribute
- see the big picture
- give up your rights
- represent the team's position, not yours
- privately and publicly affirm one another
- accept responsibility for the team's standings

Evaluate yourself:
As a team, in your opinion, do you place the team's interest above your own?

No_____Somewhat_____Yes
1   2   3   4   5   6   7   8   9   10

Jot down one or two ideas on how you can instill a sense of value in your team members while reminding them that the whole is greater than its parts.

Group Up
Why does a team need unification? Can't a strong dominant leader accomplish the same?

Group Up
Discuss in your campus group ways to increase unification and decrease competition.

6. An effective team realizes everyone plays a special role.

It is easy to start playing the comparison game when you are on a team...to feel that your role is considerably less important or valuable compared to the roles of other team members. Well, consider this:

In March of 1981, President Ronald Reagan was shot by John Hinckley, Jr., and was hospitalized for several weeks. Although Reagan was the nation's chief executive, his hospitalization had little impact on the nation's activity. Government and civil life continued.

On the other hand, suppose the garbage collectors in this country went on strike, as they did in Philadelphia years ago. That city was not only in a literal mess, the pile of decaying trash quickly became a health hazard. A three-week nationwide strike would paralyze the U.S.

This story leaves us to wonder: Who is more important—the President or a garbage collector? Scripture tells us to stop asking that question. We are all necessary, and often the most insignificant parts of the body of Christ are the most indispensable (see 1 Cor. 12)!

Evaluate yourself:

As a team, do we understand and appreciate the role of others? Where are you on the scale?

No				Somewhat					Yes
1	2	3	4	5	6	7	8	9	10

7. An effective team has a strong bench.

Think about the purpose of the bench in sports. It is not just a place to sit for supporting players who are not on the floor, but it serves a variety of other purposes as well. It is a place for strategy—at a time-out, the team huddles at the bench and figures out the strategy for the next play. It is a place for rest—when a player on the floor gets tired, she sits out on the bench to catch her breath while another player goes in for her. It is a place for encouragement—team members on the bench cheer their fellow players on and encourage them to keep going. And it is a place for assistance—whether getting signals from the coach to the players on the floor or receiving first aid, it is the place where team members look for help. The bench is a place that represents both unity and depth.

In Christian ministry, THE BENCH represents...
- Support players
- Special role players
- A place for strategy
- A place for rest
- A place for encouragement
- A place for assistance

Even nature understands this principle of unification. Researchers have found that when the roots of trees touch each other, there is a substance present that reduces competition. In fact, this unknown fungus helps link the roots of different trees—even of dissimilar species. A whole forest may be linked together. If one tree has access to water, another to nutrients, and a third to sunlight, the trees have a means to share with one another. They actually help each other.

What's Your Attitude?

For a team to work, whether on the floor or on the bench, it is important to maintain the proper attitude. Here are the attitudes to avoid if a team wants to be effective.

"The main ingredient to stardom is the rest of the team."

—John Wooden

Wrong Attitudes of Players on the Floor	**Wrong Attitudes of Players on the Bench**
• "We're more important."	• "I don't have to be ready."
• "We don't need them."	• "I don't have to pay attention."
• "I don't want to sit down."	• "I'm not contributing to the team."

If these attitudes are present on a team, it moves away from a "we" mentality to an "us against them" mentality. A team that has a good bench does not use it as a distinguishing point between team members. There is no better and best on the team, whether you are on the floor or on the bench. The bench is not a point of division, but it is a necessary place of support and strategy.

Evaluate yourself:
I would guess that as a team, I would question that we have a strong bench.

No_____Somewhat _____Yes
1   2   3   4   5   6   7   8   9   10

How can your team develop a better "bench"?

8. An effective team knows exactly where the team stands.
A team knows where it stands because there is a scoreboard that everyone can see. Players glance at the scoreboard continually during a game to measure their progress. When the game is over, at least they know if they've won or lost.

What's the Score?

Imagine you are at a basketball game. The players are running up and down the court, shooting the ball, blocking shots, and every once in a while one team steals the ball from the other. Everything seems normal in this game except one thing...there's no rim on the backboard. The players shoot the ball, but we can only guess whether or not the ball would have gone in. At halftime no one knows for sure what the score is—it is all speculation.

Sounds absurd doesn't it? What team would continue to play in such a game? It is no more absurd than when we function as a Christian team, but have no way of measuring our success.

What areas should be on your "scoreboard"? What results let you know that you are winning as a Christian team? List four.

Evaluate yourself:
As a team, do we score well in these areas?

No_____Somewhat _____Yes
1   2   3   4   5   6   7   8   9   10

9. An effective team pays the price.

There is no success without sacrifice. If I succeed without sacrifice, then it is because someone who went before me made the sacrifice. If I sacrifice and don't see success, then someone who follows me will reap success from my sacrifice.

Great teams have a "whatever-it-takes" attitude. They will pay the price they need to in order to accomplish their goals. Championship teams always have stories of how teammates played with injuries, or helped each other to compensate for temporary weaknesses. The same is true for your Christian teams.

Here is an account from Stu Webber that illustrates the need for sacrifice on a team: "We'd been running every day, but this was something else. We'd been sweating from the time we rolled out of the rack before daybreak, but now moisture drained from every pore in our bodies. Sure, this was the physical training stage of U.S. Army Ranger School, and we expected exertion—even exhaustion. But this was no morning PT rah-rah run in T-shirts.

"We ran in full field uniform. As usual, the word was, 'You go out together, you stick together, you work as a unit, and you come in together. If you don't come in together, don't bother to come in!'

"Somewhere along the way, through a fog of pain, thirst, and fatigue, my brain registered something strange about our formation. Two rows ahead of me, I noticed one of the guys out of sync—a big, rawboned redhead named Sanderson. His legs were pumping, but he was out of step with the rest of us. Then his head began to loll from side to side. This guy was struggling, close to losing it.

"Without missing a step, the Ranger on Sanderson's right reached over and took the distressed man's rifle. Now one of the Rangers was packing two weapons—his own and Sanderson's. The big redhead did better for a time. But then, while the platoon kept moving, his jaw became slack, his eyes glazed, and his legs pushed like pistons. Soon his head began to sway again.

"This time, the Ranger on the left reached over, removed Sanderson's helmet, tucked it under his own arm, and continued to run. All systems go. Our boots thudded along the dirt trail in heavy unison. Tromp-tromp-tromp-tromp-tromp-tromp.

"Sanderson was hurting, really hurting. He was buckling, going down. But no, two soldiers behind him lifted the pack off his back, each taking a shoulder strap in his free hand. Sanderson gathered his remaining strength, squared his shoulders. And the platoon continued to run. All the way to the finish line.

"We left together. We returned together. And all of us were the stronger for it. Together is better."[4]

Evaluate yourself:

As a team, is our sacrifice sufficient to provide success to the next generation?

No_____Somewhat _____Yes
1   2   3   4   5   6   7   8   9   10

Can you think of some blessings you have received that you did not pay for? Have others on the campus carried your pack? Write it down in the space provided, if possible.

What sacrifice will we make so that the next generation of Christian students on your campus will have success? Make a commitment to at lease one sacrifice. Jot it down here.

10. An effective team says yes to the right questions.
The final component to discovering whether or not your team is effective is in being able to answer yes to the right questions. There are ten questions that every team should ask...and hopefully get a yes to. Let's see how your team does...

1. Do we trust each other?

2. Do we have concern for each other?

3. Do team members feel free to communicate openly?

4. Do we understand our team's goals?

5. Do we have a commitment to those goals?

6. Do we make good use of each member's abilities?

7. Do we handle conflict successfully?

8. Does everyone participate?

9. Do we respect our individual differences?

10. Do we like being members of this team?

Review your evaluation. How effective are you as a team? How effective are you as a Christian team?

In what areas are you weak? What can you do to make your team more effective?

All for One, and One for All

A few years ago, the Special Olympics were held in the Pacific Northwest. Hundreds of families traveled to watch their special children compete to win medals. One race became an object lesson in teamwork for everyone.

Nine runners lined up at the starting blocks, each of them hoping to win the gold medal in the 400-meter race. When the gun fired, they took off. They were in a dead heat, when one of the runners fell. He was shaken up, but brushed himself off and attempted to catch up to the rest of the pack. In his haste, however, he stumbled and fell again. This time, he recognized there was no way to win the race. He couldn't even catch up to the pack. So he just sat there and began to cry.

One by one, the rest of the runners heard him crying. Within a moment, each of them stopped running and turned their attention toward their comrade. Suddenly, without any encouragement, they all sprinted across the grass to their fellow runner and helped him up from the track. Each of them hugged him, then they did something unforgettable. They all joined hands and started toward the finish line. They decided to finish the race together.

The crowd was stunned. Everyone quietly pondered who was going to get the medals. Suddenly, they broke out into applause. They realized it didn't matter. These physically and mentally challenged kids had taught the "normal" people a huge lesson on teamwork.

Assess Yourself

Place a check in the appropriate spaces below. Does your team ...

_____ Care for one another?
_____ Know and practice what's important?
_____ Grow together?
_____ Have a chemistry that fits?
_____ Place an individual's rights below the team's best interests?

_____ Realize everyone plays a special role?
_____ Have a strong bench?
_____ Know exactly where the team stands?
_____ Pay the price?
_____ Say yes to the right questions?

Application

We have seen in this lesson that teamwork truly does make the dream work, and that many times teamwork is your only hope. This is especially true for Christian endeavors on the campus. When you think of your team, do images of a well-oiled machine come to mind? Maybe it is easier to think of your team if I mention an old rusty, run-down pick-up truck. I hope that is not the case, but if it is, I hope that you will take another look throughout this lesson. Look for specific things that you can do to try to revolutionize your team and increase effectiveness.

What's Your Game Plan?

THE ART OF STRATEGIC PLANNING

*"There is no wisdom, no insight, no plan that can succeed against the LORD.
The horse is made ready for the day of battle,
but victory rests with the LORD."*
—Proverbs 21:30-31

*"When there is moral rot within a nation, its government topples easily.
But with wise and knowledgeable leaders, there is stability."*
—Proverbs 28:2 (NLT)

The Silent Plan

How can you move 38,000 troops and 163,581 tons of equipment halfway around the world in 30 days? William G. Pagonis, Deputy Commanding General for Logistics, faced one of the most challenging assignments of his army career during the three-phase crisis in the Persian Gulf that began in August 1990—Desert Shield, Desert Storm, and Desert Farewell. To Pagonis, armies eat, drive, and are a "constellation of needs"—from bakers to bureaucrats, carpenters to cashiers, soldiers to counselors. The crisis required total planning from "reception of the troops with the weapons and supplies," to "onward movement to offensive positions," to "sustainment." He had to deal with problems like bottled water boiling in the desert and tires exploding in the heat. He negotiated with Saudi merchants for supplies and all this, while moving undetected bases to support General Schwarzkopf's surprise attack on Iraqi troops from the west.[1]

What was the secret to the success of General Pagonis and his staff?
Complete knowledge of the mission
Complete knowledge of their own capabilities
Constant feedback and open communication necessary to adapt to changing conditions

Many times in everyday life it is hard for us to plan. When we fail to plan it is easy to also lose knowledge of our objective as well as communication with those we are working with. Below are some questions that you can ask yourself to gauge your effectiveness in planning.

Questions to ask before planning
Choose and circle one of the three options for each question.

Do I have complete knowledge of my mission?	NO	SOMEWHAT	YES
Do I have complete knowledge of my capabilities?	NO	SOMEWHAT	YES
Do I have complete knowledge of my team's capabilities?	NO	SOMEWHAT	YES
Do I receive constant feedback and open communication?	NO	SOMEWHAT	YES
Do I use this information to adapt and change when necessary?	NO	SOMEWHAT	YES

This Is Planning

Planning is not an attempt to foretell the future. Planning is an attempt to regulate and shape the future, and to prepare to negotiate unforeseen circumstances to one's advantage. Good planning contemplates how a current decision is going to affect the future environment. John Maxwell created a list of steps that help us remember how to lay plans.[2] PLAN AHEAD is an acronym that can help you understand some of the components to planning more efficiently.

P – Predetermine a course of action.

This is your big picture target or purpose. It will be impossible to get somewhere if you don't have a starting point and direction.

L – Lay out your goals.

Next, you must set some goals. Having goals that can be seen is paramount. If you don't understand your goals, neither will anyone else. Put them on paper.

A – Adjust your priorities.

We are all busy, it's just part of our culture. But planning ahead is about finding the most important things in your schedule. Put your goals in the right order of priority. Focus on them.

N – Notify key personnel.

Now you must communicate with key people on your team. Part of planning is making sure everyone knows what part of the plan he or she should participate in.

A – Allow time for acceptance.

Leaders have the ability to see ahead. Unfortunately, not everyone does. It is important for you to give your plan time to gain acceptance, and allow others to commit.

H – Head into action.

Next, it is time to act. It was once said that some dream of worthy accomplishments while others stay awake and do them. Implement wisely and deliberately.

E – Expect problems.

Problems always occur when we plan anything. Your success will depend not on avoiding these problems, but instead will depend on dealing with them effectively as they arise.

A – Always point to your successes.

Looking to your successes will continually encourage you, as well as the people you lead. Remembering what God has done in the past will help you toward your goal.

D – Daily review your planning.

One practice many students had in the past was making out a daily schedule. Budget every hour wisely, then assess what you accomplished at the end of the day.[3]

Reflect and Respond ...

Reflect on whether planning is hard for you? Why or why not? Jot down one or two reasons in the space below.

Group Up

Discuss in your group some of the different outcomes of those who plan and those who don't.

How well do you follow the "PLAN AHEAD" model? Where are you the strongest? weakest?

Strengths

Weaknesses

Biblical Examples of Planning

We need to remember that planning itself does not "quench the Holy Spirit." It is a biblical practice. In fact, even God plans His activities. Below are just a few examples of planning that take place in the Bible. Take a look at this biblical basis for planning and see how planning was utilized in each example.

God Did It ...

"Have you not heard? Long ago I ordained it, In days of old I planned it; now I have brought it to pass..." (Isa. 37:26). In this verse we see God speaking through the prophet Isaiah, saying that He had earlier planned the events that were just then coming to pass.

Noah Did It ...

Noah received explicit instructions from God to build the ark. God gave detailed measurements to Noah, who was faithful to carry out the long-range plan. He finished the ark's construction exactly as God told him—in 120 years. It was built so well that it with-stood 40 days of torrential rain, then floated a solid year as the floods subsided (see Gen. 7—9).

Nehemiah Did It ...

The long-range plan of Nehemiah was to see the wall of Jerusalem rebuilt. He visualized the completion of the wall, then began plans for its construction. The work was completed in 52 days because each family was assigned a certain portion of the wall to build. He planned and organized the project with excellence (see Neh. 1-5).

David Did It ...

The long-range plan of David was to build a temple (see 2 Sam. 7). God did not allow David to build it because of his associations with wars (see 1 Kings 5:2-3). However, when Solomon was chosen to succeed him, David handed Solomon the completed plan for the temple and a list of materials on hand. After seven years of construction, the temple was completed, and the long-range plan of David was fulfilled.

Jesus Told Parables About It ...

We often fail to notice that Jesus frequently spoke about the necessity of planning and strategy. In fact, in two of His parables, He told stories about how foolish it is to neglect it:

The Wise and Foolish Builder (Matt. 7:24-27)
The Builder Counting the Cost (Luke 14:28-30)
The King Planning for Battle (Luke 14:31-32)
The Unjust Steward (Luke 16:1-8)

"Doing the same thing over and over, expecting different results is the definition of crazy."
—unknown

How does your planning correspond to those in the Bible related to planning or are they just thrown together? In your planning for collegiate projects, how are you like:

God?

Noah?

Nehemiah?

David?

Jesus?

Barriers to Planning

Most of us understand the need for planning, but inevitably we seem to be blocked by a barrier that keeps us from it. Knowing and understanding the barrier is the first step to overcoming it. Take a look at this list and see which ones could be blocking you.

1. It involves change—Usually, the greater the changes, the greater the resistance. We have probably all experienced this in one way or another on the campus. It is easy to for us to get into a set pattern in life, and planning will usually move us away from that pattern and into a realm of change. When we do create change, many people will resent it and fight against it.

2. Situations change—The longer the projection and the larger the project, the greater the need for flexibility. Life seems to always find a way of throwing us a curve ball. Things happen that are beyond our control. If we want to accomplish our goals, we must learn to be flexible and to adapt.

3. Leadership ego—"Only rarely are business failures or poor decisions the result of too much planning; almost universally they can be traced to management ego—the temptation to say, 'I don't need a plan; I'm sure I can handle whatever develops'" (Richard S. Sloma).

4. Different perspectives—Everyone looks at the situation through their own lenses—they understand situations via their own context, values, ability, and benefits. This doesn't always make for harmony. God made us different, not to compete with each other but to complete each other.

5. Lack of good thinkers—"Where success is concerned, people are not measured in inches or pounds or college degrees or family background. They are measured by the size of their thinking" (David Schwartz).

TWO TYPES OF THINKERS NEEDED IN PLANNING:

CRITICAL THINKERS (They ask: "What needs to be changed?")
CREATIVE THINKERS (They ask: "How can we change it?")

Group Up
Why do we need both critical and creative thinkers as we lead on campus?

6. Planning becomes the end (not the means)—Planning is not enough. Action must accompany it. Planning is a continual process. Doing it once doesn't make a successful organization. Good organization provides a good structure. Great organizations provide good structure and motivation.

7. Uncertainty of the future—This is maybe the toughest barrier of all. It's difficult to plan because we just don't know what tomorrow holds. Let's face it. It is easier to respond to an emergency than a probability. Legislatures (and most founders or donors to the school) more readily appropriate money to repair a disaster than prevent one.

Planning and the Sigmoid Curve

Many times as leaders we make changes only when we have to, or when it is obvious. But in strategic planning we start the planning process before we may see the need for change. The "sigmoid curve" is a great example of seeing the need to plan. It was conceived by British educator Charles Handy. Without planning and strategy the leader can never anticipate trouble earlier than it arrives. When a leader plans, he is not only preparing his organization for this one task but also for the opportunity to look ahead and continue development.

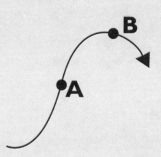

Change Before You Have To

If there were not a need for change in the organization, there would be no need for leaders. One thing that determines your effectiveness as a leader is your ability to recognize when it's time to change. The diagram to the right indicates that as corporations grow, they rise in a fashion similar to the arrow. When the arrow is at its peak, production has peaked for the organization in its present mode of operation.

Most leaders and corporations don't recognize the need for change until Point B, when production has begun to decline. Handy argues that leaders must have the foresight to predict trends, and change before decline sets in, at Point A. This is difficult, because no one else in the organization sees a need to "fix" what isn't broken.

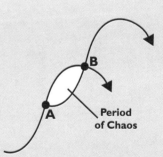

Be Ready for a Period of Chaos

If as a leader you make the change at Point A, you will incur the misunderstanding of others. Then, for the season between Point A and Point B, your organization will experience a period of "chaos" in which everyone feels they are in a state of "flux," routines have been disturbed, and the security of the familiar is absent. This chaos can only be avoided if the leader waits until it's obvious the change is needed—however, at that point, it is too late to stay on top of the game. You must change before it is obvious.

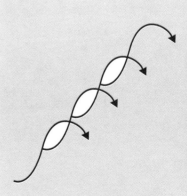

The Cost of Growth Is Constant Change

Within any organization, growth that is constant will without a doubt mean consistent chaos! Consequently, if organizations desire to stay on top, they are literally inviting chaos to be their constant companion, as in the diagram to the right. There will be a consistent trend of change, growth, and recognition for more change—and chaos. If leaders and their organizations are secure enough to endure it, this chaotic, flexible mode of operation will save their futures.

Reflect and Respond ...

As a leader on your campus, think how many of these barriers you have experienced. Did you overcome them or give in to them? Do you understand why? Jot down one idea here in the space provided.

After reflecting on the barriers, now that you know what is blocking your progress, what steps can you take to overcome these obstacles? Jot down at least two or three for future discussion.

Steps to Successful Strategic Planning

1. Plan to plan.

It is important to understand that as a leader on your campus you must plan to plan. A certain amount of time and energy must be allotted in your daily or weekly agenda for this process. This is the number-one mistake made in programs. Everyone agrees about the importance of strategic planning—but they fail in planning to plan. Let's look at the diagram below. This scenario has most likely happened to all of us. When we do very little planning, we find ourselves taking a longer amount of time for execution due to changes and unexpected events. When we spend a good deal of time planning we may feel that we are being unproductive, but, in the long run, we will actually save time on the overall task.

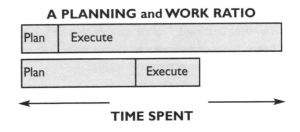

A PLANNING and WORK RATIO

Plan	Execute	
Plan		Execute

TIME SPENT

Imagine that a bank credits your account each morning with $86,400, carries over no balance from day to day, allows you to keep no cash balance, and every evening cancels whatever part of the amount you had failed to use during the day. What would you do? Draw out every cent, of course!

Well, everyone has such a bank. Its name is TIME. Every morning it credits you with 86,400 seconds. Every night it writes off as lost whatever of this time you have failed to invest to good purpose. It carries over no balance. It allows no overdraft. Each day opens a new account for you. Each night it burns the record of the day. If you fail to use the day's deposits, the loss is yours. There is no going back. There is no drawing against "tomorrow." You must live in the present of today's deposits. Invest it so as to get from it the utmost in health, happiness, and success. The clock is running. Make the most of today.

- To realize the value of one year, ask a student who has failed his final exam.
- To realize the value of one month, ask a student who has the date due changed.
- To realize the value of one week, ask the editor of a weekly newspaper.
- To realize the value of one day, ask the students who are waiting to meet.
- To realize the value of one minute, ask the student who has missed an exam.
- To realize the value of one second, ask the person who has survived an accident.
- To realize the value of one millisecond, ask the person who has won a gold medal.

Treasure every moment that you have. Time is a coin that you can spend only once. Use it, invest it, make it count, and treasure it more because you shared it with someone special ... special enough to have your time ... and remember, time waits for no one. Grab it and use it wisely day after day.

2. Determine your primary purpose.
Ask yourself:
   What is the chief purpose we are trying to accomplish?
   Why do we exist?
   What is the reason we are doing what we are doing?

A business man walked to lunch downtown. On his way, he saw some construction workers building a tall structure. He wondered at it, amazed at its potential beauty. Then he decided to ask one of them what it was they were building.

"What are you doing?" he asked a worker.

"I am laying bricks," the worker mumbled.

Not getting his answer, he asked a second worker the same question. The worker grumbled his reply, "I am drawing a paycheck."

Still not getting the answer he was after, the man asked a third worker what he was doing. With a twinkle in his eye, he looked up and said: "I'm building a cathedral."

Only one worker saw the big picture. He alone saw his role in the light on the overall purpose—and it made a difference in his subtle attitude.

Purposeful organizations require two types of planning:

- **Strategic Planning:** deals with the broad purposes and objectives of the organization, its character and personality. It's usually long term and big-picture oriented.

- **Operational Planning:** deals with short-range goals and decisions, usually covers a short time span, and is the function of lower management. This is the daily grind.

Group Up
How can we be sure that as students we always remember to value our time?

Many students have both of these thought patterns, but often their position and personality will cause them to lean toward one or the other. It is important to remember that both of these ways of thinking are essential. Which way of thinking do you lean toward? What is the best way to make up for what you lack?

3. Assess the situation.

"Strategy is first trying to understand where you sit in today's world—not where you wish you were or where you hoped you would be, but where you are. Then it's trying to understand where you want to be five years out. Finally, it's assessing the realistic changes of getting from here to there" (Jack Welch, Jr., Chairman of General Electric). Jack Welch understood strategy, but he also understood that a plan for the future based on an unrealistic view of the present will inevitably lead to disaster. One way to verify that we are seeing the situation clearly is to look at it from different angles. Take our eyes, for example. Two eyes give depth perception because each eye sees the picture from a different angle. In the same way, we can have a clearer idea of our present situation when we look at it from more than one angle. Listed below are four angles that you may find helpful when assessing your situation.

From INSIDE the organization
See what you are doing from the perspective of those you work with.

From a CURRENT point of view
What does your situation look like from where you are now?

From OUTSIDE the organization
See what you are doing from the perspective of someone who does not know about your strategy.

From a FUTURE point of view
What does your situation look like months or years from now? What TRENDS are developing?

Group Up

Do you tend to be more of a strategic planner or an operational planner? As you plan on campus through your many commitments, what are the strengths and weaknesses of each approach?

Reflect and Respond ...

Do you think using this method of looking at different angles would help you improve making a strategy? How? Reflect and jot down two or three reasons for your thinking.

1.

2.

3.

What are some needs that need to be addressed in your leadership NOW? In the FUTURE? See if you can list some of the needs in the space provided.

4. Prioritize the needs.

Be sure there is agreement within the team on what goals are most important. As a team, list them in the order of importance and priority. When we do not prioritize or improperly prioritize, we leave results to chance. More often than not, the easy things will get done, but the important things will not. We tend to do the urgent things, but not the important. The problem is that when we forget the ultimate, we become a slave to the immediate.

5. Ask the right questions.

The fifth step is being sure you are asking the right questions. As Christian leaders we need to ask questions, especially the tough ones In doing this, we force ourselves to think on a higher level. If we continue to do this, we will always be able to stay on task in completing our mission. In the past, you may have had trouble with this because you did not know what questions to ask. In my studies I have come down to **ten basic questions** that you will find useful.

a. **MARKET:**

Who are we trying to serve and what needs are we meeting?

b. **LEADERSHIP:**

Do we have the right people at the top to accomplish our goals?

c. **COUNSEL:**

Whose advice do we need in order to succeed?

d. **DIRECTION:**

Exactly what are we going to do short-range, mid-range, and long-range?

e. **ORGANIZATION:**

Who's responsible for what? Who will supervise whom?

f. **CASH:**

What are our expected expenses and income?

g. **REPORTING:**

Are we on target?

h. **COMMUNICATION:**

How can we effectively make known what we're doing?

i. **EVALUATING:**

Are we seeking the quality we expect or demand from ourselves?

j. **REFINING:**

How can we keep improving in the critical aspects of this project or service?

That's Impossible!

When leaders ask the right questions, the results are astounding. They gain the ability to reach goals that others think are impossible. If we fail to ask the right questions, we'll become short-sighted and miss future success. Take a look at some of these quotes about the "impossible."

Group Up

In light of these quotes, what impossible things do you think you want to accomplish on campus? What does God want to accomplish?

"I think there may be a world market for maybe five computers."
-Thomas Watson, chairman of IBM, 1943

"Everything that can be invented has been invented."
-Charles H. Duell, Commissioner, U.S. Office of Patents, 1899

"Drill for oil? You mean drill into the ground to try and find oil? You're crazy."
-Drillers who Edwin L. Drake tried to enlist to his project to drill for oil in 1859

"We don't like their sound, and guitar music is on the way out."
-Decca Recording Co. rejecting the Beatles, 1962

Christian leadership is not about prioritizing your schedule, but scheduling your priorities.

6. Set specific goals.

In the course of Christian planning you will find it useful if you set specific goals for accomplishing what God puts in front of you. These goals will help you see the steps to take in reaching your goals. In order for a Christian goal to be reached, it must conform to the following criteria. It must be ...

a. WRITTEN
Write out what you know God wants to accomplish. It will serve as a daily reminder and viewable goal of what is to be completed next.

b. SPECIFIC
A general plan may be easy to formulate, but when it comes down to completing the goal, the objectives will be fuzzy and discouraging. Be specific with your plans.

c. REALISTIC
Set goals that you feel God can help you reach. Although it may be exhilarating when you first set lofty goals, you need to remember that a goal is only worthwhile if it is completed.

d. MEASURABLE
A measurable goal is important because it allows you to evaluate how well you are doing. Make goals so that you can keep track of how well you are doing as you implement God's plan on your campus.

e. PERSONAL
Personal goals are goals that have ownership. They need to connect at the heart level related to your relationship to Christ, and inspire emotion.

f. CONVICTIONAL
Christian-based goals need to be addressing a real problem, an issue that you are willing to put an investment in because of your relationship with Christ.

7. Clarify and communicate.

How often have you sat through a productive planning session in your BCM or church college group, left the meeting enthused about results, yet nothing ever materialized? A specific link exists between planning and implementation—the link is communication and clarification. Communication is sharing a vision of the objective that is to be accomplished. Clarification is showing the steps that need to be followed. This does not mean specifically telling another student what to do, but giving guidelines to stay within when completing the goal.

8. Identify possible obstacles.

The next step is identifying possible obstacles. At this point you are actually doing negative thinking. Think of obstacles that might occur so you can develop ways to overcome them. Remember that Satan is at work in your life as actively as God. Imagine a "worst case scenario" and how you can keep it under control with God's guidance. Remember the planning and work ratio on page 54. This is the same concept. You can avoid many of the obstacles that would normally take up your time and push you farther away from completing your goal with simple planning and a little forethought. When you take the time to plan more, it will take less time to execute.

The most important prerequisite before implementing a plan: "The Mental Walk Through." Mentally walk through the entire goal or event you're planning with God's direction to note anything you might have forgotten.

The most important result of any planning meeting: "The Next Steps."

Determine the next steps you must take to accomplish the goal God has led you to make.

Reflect and Respond ...

Have you ever done this? If you haven't, take a few minutes to think these things through. Ask yourself, *"How will I accomplish this goal I feel God wants me to complete?"* Examine these three questions and answer them to the best of your ability.

When is the next time I can put these things God wants into practice?

How can I improve laying out the next steps for my team according to godly principles?

How can I give freedom to my team and empower them to accomplish their goal in Christ?

Group Up
Would you rather be a military commander, CEO, coach, or a poet/gardener in your leadership on campus? Why?

9. Have an open system of planning.

You also need to have an open-system approach in your planning. As you listen to God, you have to experience an open-system approach. An open system is sympathetic to its environment; it allows external entities to influence the decision-making and planning process. A closed system attempts to exist with no regard to concerns outside itself. This says, *God, don't bother me. I'm comfortable doing it this way.*

The Evolution of Leadership

a. The military commander
Fifty years ago, when we spoke of leadership in America, it conjured up a military image. Even our presidents were former officers. It was a top-down model. Leaders led; followers obeyed.

b. The CEO
In the 1970s, a new perspective emerged. A more popular view of leadership was the CEO, where the leader led through a shared vision, not merely driven by the leader's personal preferences. Everyone was to catch the vision and become inspired to help fulfill it. Although the vision was exciting for everyone, it was still a top-down model.

c. The coach
In the late 1980s and early 1990s a new paradigm surfaced for leadership. It was the leader as a coach; the staff was a team who played important positions. Emphasis was on using gifts to reach a common goal. This was a big improvement, but it was still top-down. Have we gotten to the leadership paradigm you practice yet?

d. The poet and the gardener
As we move into the 21st century, emerging leaders have new expectations. Both young leaders and young followers reject the top-down models. However, they long to be part of something that will make a difference. The emerging leader can be likened to a "poet." Think about good poets you know. What makes them good is that they simply put clear, heartfelt words to things you have felt and thought yourself. You found yourself saying, *"Yes! I agree with that. That's what I feel, too."* In this leadership model, the leader doesn't have to have all the answers, but simply listens to what the Holy Spirit seems to be saying to the leadership team—then puts words to it. He clearly articulates the dream. It is a team effort—not just the work, but the vision itself.

The metaphor of the "gardener" is also a good one for the emerging leader. Today leaders must see themselves as developers of people through the guidance of the Holy Spirit, similar to gardeners, whose job is to grow plants. A good gardener pulls the weeds, cultivates the soil, and builds an atmosphere conducive to growing plants to their maximum potential. This is the kind of leader people will follow in the future, one who grows the people in his or her care.

10. Manage and direct your resources.
Outside of students on your campus, your most valuable assets are time and money. Invest both wisely and specifically.

Schedule—Put your items on a schedule that is responsible yet productive. Without a schedule you can't keep on track, both on campus and in your church.

Budget—Make a budget. Determine the cost of the project, and at what point costs will be incurred. Attempt to remove any surprises you possibly can! Your campus director will love you. The chairman of the finance committee at church will love you.

11. Monitor and correct.
The life of an organization moving through time is like a canoe trip down a large river. Regardless of how conscientiously plans are made, there is a constant need for monitoring and correction if the final destination is to be reached. This is true for you as you lead on campus and in your church and community.

This is also demonstrated in the world of flying. When you get into an airplane, the pilot has a flying plan, like all of us need in every project that we wish to accomplish. But once in the air, the flight plan really turns into a string of adjustments until you reach the ground again. The pilot spends all the time in the air adjusting the plane so that it stays on track with the flight plan. Your goals during college will be the same way. Always have a plan to begin with but have the understanding that the minute you stop adjusting and making changes, your course will be altered and you will get off track. Have you changed your major?

12. Study the results.

"Keeping score" is the only way to know if you're winning or losing as you become a campus leader. Develop vehicles to keep score. If you're going to make changes—you ought to do it off of current information. This will help you stay on top of the project. Like the Sigmoid Curve, as a leader you have to be at least one step ahead; you have to see changes that need to be made before they have to be made. When you are able to study the results, you create this opportunity for yourself. In doing this, you can make the most out of the time God has given you.

Obviously, you can make plans, but the results are up to the Lord. Only He knows the future. Only He controls the resources. Only He can pull off a miracle—and sometimes that's exactly what you'll need as a leader.

Consider one of the biggest arithmetical miracles in the world:

Moses and the people were in the desert, but what was he going to do with them?

They had to be fed, and feeding three million people requires a lot of food. According to the Quartermaster General in the Army, it is reported that Moses would have to have had 1,500 tons of food each day. Do you know that to bring that much food each day, two freight trains each a mile long would be required?

Besides, you must remember that they were in the desert, and they would have to have firewood to use in cooking the food. This would take 4,000 tons of wood and a few more freight trains each a mile long, just for one day. And just think, they were 40 years in transit.

Oh, yes, they would have to have water. If they only had enough to drink and wash a few dishes, it would take 11,000,000 gallons each day and a freight train with tank cars 1,800 miles long, just to bring water.

And then another thing. They had to get across the Red Sea at night. Now if they went on a narrow path, double file, the line would be 800 miles long and would require 35 days and nights to get through. So there had to be a space in the Red Sea three miles wide so they could walk 5,000 abreast to get over in one night.

But then another problem surfaced: Each time they camped at the end of the day, a campground two-thirds the size of the state of Rhode Island was required, or a total of 750 square miles long. Think of it—this space just for nightly camping!

Do you think Moses figured all this out before he left Egypt? I think not! You see, Moses believed in God. He trusted God for the details he could not foresee.

Let us take courage—we have the same God. We think our leadership problems are so big. Remember what God can do, what He has done! Team up with God and your problems will be His. Let Him run your life.

This is the best game plan of all!

Guided Prayer
Lord,
Thank You for these steps, reminding me how I can plan as a Christian leader on campus, and for my facilitators and their willingness to invest in my life.

Give me opportunities to use the principles that I am learning in this lesson. Let excellence be in all that I do as a leader, and all that I am. Thank You, Father.

Amen.

Assess Yourself

In this lesson we have discussed the benefit of planning and strategy. Below I have added a checklist for you to go over. Look at the list during this week and when you have evaluated each component of your game plan, mark it off. Be thorough in your investigation.

I plan to plan.

I have determined my primary purpose.

I have assessed our situation.

I have prioritized the needs of my team.

I have asked the right questions.

I have set specific goals.

I have clarified and communicated the goals of our team.

I have implemented an open system of planning.

I have focused my schedule.

I have consulted with my budget.

I have monitored and corrected our plans.

I have studied the results.

I have sought God's direction in all the above.

Application

Depending on where you are on your leadership journey as a Christian, you may be able to use many of these principles or just a few. Whatever the case, remember that your goal should be to make yourself the most effective leader/team that you can be for God. Only in doing this will you gain maximum effectiveness as a Christian leader.

You Can Become an Effective Communicator

LEARNING TO SPEAK THE LANGUAGE OF LEADERSHIP

"Who gave man his mouth? Who makes him deaf or mute?
Who gives him sight or makes him blind? Is it not I, the LORD?"
—Exodus 4:11

"A word aptly spoken is like apples of gold in settings of silver."
—Proverbs 25:11

Becoming an Effective Communicator

Probably the most famous speech in the 20th century was not made by a politician, business leader, or Hollywood celebrity. It was made by a pastor. In 1963 Dr. Martin Luther King, Jr., stood on the steps of the Lincoln Memorial and delivered a speech that made history. He was a masterful communicator, repeating one phrase over and over, "I have a dream!" in that 17-minute speech. As America listened to him, speaking to 100,000 people on the Washington mall and countless others via television, he captured the heart of the nation. It's a speech known all over the world and still stirs people toward achieving his dream.

There is an interesting footnote to the story, though. The written manuscript Dr. King took with him to the podium was finished after 11 minutes. Once he finished his scripted speech, his intuition told him that he had not connected with the people enough to elicit action. So, after finishing his planned words, King went on speaking from the depth of his heart, and from the overflow of his reading. These essential six minutes are the most memorable. When he finished, he had connected. Martin Luther King, Jr., had cast a clear vision. In the following year, civil rights legislation was passed in Washington, D.C. His words had created a movement.[1]

Do You Copy?

As a student, you live in an age in which technology makes communication easier than ever. Through picking up a cell phone, sending an email, or getting on the Web, you can communicate information anytime and anywhere. Yet sociologists tell us that people are becoming poorer and poorer in their communication skills as time marches on into the 21st century. Why is this? It seems to me that while we have the tools to communicate, people are unwilling to work at the people skills in order to communicate effectively. This gives us all the more reason to be effective communicators ourselves. As the story above illustrates, people will follow a leader who clearly and effectively communicates truth. They want to "own" a vision, but cannot unless they first understand the vision.

Basic Truth
When we improve our abilities to communicate as collegians, we increase our abilities to lead.

Guided Prayer
Lord,
I know You have a message that You want me to communicate, but sometimes my lips fail me.
I try to say something, but become afraid that I might not connect with others. Help me to learn how to communicate better while I am still a student. Help my mind to stay sharp and focused as I go through this lesson. Bring to my mind people I need to relate to, and ways I can reach them.
Amen.

Group Up
Do you think that communication is important in your leadership as a collegian? Why?

Reflect and Respond ...

Define *communication* in your own words in the space provided below:

In your opinion and observations, what makes for good communication?

From your viewpoint, what should be the purpose of a speech? Jot down an idea here.

"One who forms a judgment upon any point, but cannot explain himself clearly to the people, might as well have never thought at all on the subject."
—Pericles

How'd He Do It?

Martin Luther King, Jr., is noted as one of the great communicators of the 20th century. He was able to motivate people to action by his words. He communicated a truth that spoke to their hearts and affirmed their value and worth as human beings. His focus was not on giving a speech, but on changing the hearts of his listeners. He would not stop speaking until this was done. This quality exemplified by Martin Luther King, Jr., is what we would call *charisma*. Charisma enables leaders to become movers and shakers among people. But what exactly is charisma, and what does it mean to be a charismatic leader?

Charisma is that magnetic attraction in certain students that motivates others and causes them to feel better about themselves. Charismatic leaders have the ability to capture their listeners through their words. Like metal to a magnet, people are drawn to leaders who exhibit charisma. Listeners are changed in how they view themselves, and are given a renewed sense of purpose and vision in life.

Consider this: Public speakers may have content, but communicators have charisma. Building your charisma level will require you to become more "people oriented" rather than "lesson oriented." Public speakers teach lessons. Communicators teach people! Note the comparison between the two.

PUBLIC SPEAKER	COMMUNICATOR
1. Puts the message before the people	1. Puts the people before the message
2. Asks the question: What do I have?	2. Asks the question: What do they need?
3. Focuses on atmosphere	3. Focuses on techniques
4. Content oriented	4. Change oriented
5. Goal: Complete the message	5. Goal: Complete the people

Communicators are focused on how their message will affect and transform their audiences. They speak to incite change, not merely to be heard. Their goal is not merely to inform students or impress students, but instead to impact students on campus and others in your church and community.

Reflect and Respond ...

Do you feel you have charisma? List one or more charismatic qualities you exhibit.

Can you think of ways to increase your charisma level? How do you demonstrate this charisma in the lives of other students?

Truths of the Trade

When it comes to communication, there are three important truths to remember:
- There are no small audiences, only small speakers.
- There are no boring subjects, only boring speakers.
- If you are interested in your audience, they will be interested in you!

You Are the Message

In his book, *You Are the Message,* Roger Ailes wrote about Captain "Red" McDaniel, a Navy pilot who was shot down in North Vietnam and held as a prisoner-of-war for six years. "Red" described his battle to communicate with both captors and captives. He knew his first impression on the enemy would make or break how they would relate in the prison camp. He made sure his face, as well as his words, communicated confidence. He then described the desperate need for prisoners to communicate with each other to maintain morale. He said POWs tend to die much sooner if they give up attempts to stay in touch with other prisoners, especially when in solitary confinement. When he was in solitary confinement, he realized how communication was a transmittal of who he was—a path between his heart and the hearts of others. Prisoners risked death to work out elaborate systems of communication. They would tap on walls, write under plates, cough, sing, laugh, scratch, or flap laundry a certain number of times to transmit a letter of the alphabet. He later wrote: "One thing I knew: I had to have communication with my people." He soon discovered this was what his Vietnamese captors took the greatest pains to prevent.[2]

When we think of survival, we think of food, water, and shelter as the essentials. It seems to me that communication might belong in that group of essentials.

Stumbling Blocks

Imagine for a moment that you have been asked to speak to a large group of your peers. You have less than seven days to prepare a message that should persuade and motivate them to action. How do you feel? How will you feel just moments before stepping up in front of the group? Nervous? Excited? Like you want to crawl into a hole and get out of the whole mess?

Psychologists say that public speaking is the number-one fear of most people. It even ranks above the fear of death! (Comedian Jerry Seinfield explains that means if you are attending a funeral, you'd rather be the guy in the casket than the guy delivering the eulogy!)

> "It's not what you tell them, it is what they hear."
> —Red Auerbach, former coach, Boston Celtics

What makes communication so difficult? What hinders our message from being heard? See below ten of the most common hurdles in communication.

- Initial rapport is not established
- Stiff body movements
- Material is presented intellectually and does not involve people emotionally
- Poor eye contact and facial expression
- Humor is lacking
- Lack of competence in the presentation
- Low energy and enthusiasm
- Boring language and material
- The message is not owned by the messenger
- Lack of audience participation

Do You Believe?

Have you heard a speaker who has tripped over any of these hurdles? Or have you tripped over any of these yourself? These hurdles tend to originate from a lack of belief. In order to overcome these hurdles in communication, you've got to ...

◆ Believe in God. Believe in the call God has given you, and His ability to empower you.

◆ Believe in yourself. Believe that you have the gifts and abilities to carry out God's call.

◆ Believe in your subject. Believe that what you have to say is worth hearing.

◆ Believe in your audience. Believe they can and will rise to the challenge of your message.

Reflect and Respond ...

Of the ten hurdles listed above, which do you find are the hardest for you to overcome? What can you do to overcome these?

As you think about yourself as a communicator, which of the four beliefs listed above are difficult for you? If you want, jot the four down here. You can even write just the number.

What can you do to strengthen your belief in these areas while on campus?

"The words of the wise are like goads, their collected sayings like firmly imbedded nails—given by one Shepherd" (Eccl. 12:11).

The Great Communicator

Among the great communicators in history, Jesus is noted for His ability to connect with people. But how did He do it? Jesus built bridges of relationships that could bear the weight of truth. Note how in Matthew 13 He communicated with others:

1. Simplify the message (vv. 3,10-13)
It's not what you say, but how you say it. Jesus wasn't superficial, but He was simple. He told stories everyone could relate to. He took what was complicated and made it simple.

2. See the person (vv. 1-2,9)
It is not what you say, but how they see it. Jesus was faced with a large and varied audience. He knew them well enough to speak their language and help them understand.

3. Seize the moment (vv. 2,14-17)
It's not what you say, but when you say it. Verse 2 tells us when the people came, Jesus spoke. He waited until they showed initiative. When they rejected, He withdrew.

4. Show the truth (v. 54)
It's not what you say, but how you show it. Jesus didn't merely use words. He demonstrated credibility with His life and miracles. He proved He could be trusted.

5. Seek the responsive (v. 51)
It's not what you say, but how they respond to it. After Jesus taught, He asked, "Do you understand these things?" Jesus always gave people something new to think, feel, and do.

Group Up
Can you think of anything else that Jesus utilized to be more effective in His communication as a leader?

Reflect and Respond ...

What strikes you most about Jesus' method of communication?

How can you use these lessons from Jesus to become a better communicator on your campus?

Real Life

Only one U.S. president was commonly called, "the great communicator"—Ronald Reagan. You may remember, Reagan was an actor and understood what it means to connect with an audience. He had the ability to disarm his listeners with a genuine smile, quick wit, and sense of humor. Often, he would find himself in a sticky situation in which people with opposing views confronted him with issues that had no easy answer. Inevitably, he would find a way to respond, relieve the tension, and move on. This happened during his second presidential debate with Walter Mondale. His age became the issue. In his seventies, Reagan was asked by a reporter if he was too old to be president. He smiled and said: "I want you to know that I am not going to make age an issue in this campaign. I will not, for any political purposes, exploit my opponent's youth and inexperience." Everyone laughed, and they moved on with the rest of the debate. Another time, Reagan was questioned about his age and he responded, "It's true, I am 70. But remember that's only 36 Celsius." He was a great communicator.[3]

Timing Is Everything

Like Ronald Reagan, a great communicator has the ability to think on his or her feet. They are not spitting out a memorized script, but they know the subject well enough to allow for spontaneity in the delivery. Here are some tips that will help you develop this skill of timing:

- Be audience oriented.
- Be impact-conscience rather than image-conscience.
- Remember—pauses can be golden.
- Develop enough confidence to take risks.
- Play off of creative ideas that emerge during the session.
- Be authentic—catch a pair of eyes with each thought.
- Build a responsive audience over time.

The Great Ones

If you think about the extraordinary communicators during the last century, they practiced the qualities on the list above. They connected with their audiences. They took risks. They were real and passionate. They knew how to focus on making an impact in their speeches.

Franklin Roosevelt used to have "fireside chats" with America. He would converse with them in front of a fire, over a radio, during the dark days of the 1930s and 40s. Winston Churchill would strike at the emotions of the British, and fire up their hearts to stand against Hitler and the Nazis. John F. Kennedy challenged America to think beyond their neighborhoods. In 1961, he promised to put a man on the moon by the end of the decade. Martin Luther King, Jr., spoke honestly about the fight for equal rights and said it wouldn't be easy. He then said, "But I have been to the mountaintop, and I have seen the promised land." His challenge moved his listeners even after he died.

Great leaders communicate in the right way at the right time with the right people.

Thirty Seconds or Less

Communication means to both speak and listen. The word *communication* comes from the Latin *communico,* meaning *share.*

If you only had thirty seconds to communicate your point to another student, how would you do it? Does that sound like an impossible task? In his book, *How to Get Your Point Across in Thirty Seconds or Less,* Milo Frank shares these insights to help us connect:

1. Have an objective
Know walking into the speech what you are hoping to achieve once you are done. You cannot hit a bull's eye unless you know your target. Clearly define in your own mind the main point you are trying to communicate so that you do not wander when you are giving your speech.

2. Know your listener
Be familiar with your audience and what their needs are. Because each audience is different and has different needs, you need to ensure that your message is relevant and your method of communication is effective.

3. Choose the best approach
By recognizing that every audience is different, the obvious conclusion is that one approach that may work for one group may not work for another. Imagine trying to effectively communicate a message to a group of junior-highers by lecturing at them the entire time. Horrible images come into your mind, I am sure. You will quickly lose your listeners if you do not take the time to evaluate what approach will be most effective.

4. Use a "hook"

A "hook" is a tangible idea the audience can grab hold of and apply. It is usually an action point. It is measurable, realistic, and yet challenging. It is always something that grabs the audience, makes them want to listen, and causes them to remember what you've said.

5. Develop the subject

Expand enough on your subject so that it is clear to the audience as well as meaningful and relevant to their lives. Demonstrate that you've done your homework and that you know what you are talking about.

6. Paint a picture

People think in pictures. People need a "point" for their head, and a "picture" for their heart. Get them to connect with what you are saying through creating images in their minds that are relevant to your point. Use either stories or word pictures.

7. Ask for what you want

Leave your audience with a charge. Challenge them to take action. If you don't ask, they may not know how you want them to respond.

Group Up
Do you feel capable of doing all of these seven things as a student? Which do you do the best with your leadership style?

Your Delivery

We've all experienced it: The professor whose lectures are so boring that their monotone voice leaves you struggling to keep your eyes open. Or the Bible study speaker who makes you so confused by big words and drawn out explanations that you are forced to doodle to make some good use of your time.

The way in which you deliver your message will greatly impact other's reception of it. The following list of imperatives serves as a great starting point as you plan to deliver your message. These practical guides can turn a good message into a great one.

- Grab the listeners' attention with a sharp statement, story, fact, or Scripture.
- Be enthusiastic and bold—be excited about your message.
- Keep it simple and clear—don't be too wordy.
- Mix up the tone and the volume of your speaking.
- Be visual—use audiovisuals whenever possible.
- Use your whole body—move around.
- Present a "bottom line" you want them to act on.

Reflect and Respond ...

As a communicator on your campus, which of the following aspects of delivery listed above do you feel you already practice fairly well? Which guide do you struggle with?

What can you do to develop your delivery in the areas in which you struggle?

Sometimes the difference between "good communication" and "great communication" is the little extras that you employ to gain confidence—confidence in yourself, and in the hearts and minds of the listener. The following are simple tidbits I have picked up that have reduced anxiety and improved my ability to connect with the audience. They are little tricks of the trade, secrets of communication, I wish someone had told me sooner.

Ten Ways to Reduce Anxiety as a Speaker[4]

1. Prepare extensively

Proper prior planning prevents pitiful poor performance. Don't be caught off guard. Allow yourself enough time to sufficiently prepare so when the time comes to speak, you will be confident in the message you have to give. Winston Churchill said, "There is in the act of preparing the moment you start caring." Don't rely on your ability to "wing it." If you care about your message, you will take time to prepare.

> "Proper prior planning prevents pitiful, poor performance."
> —Winston Churchill

Reflect and Respond ...

List several things you can do to ensure that you are well prepared for speaking.

1.

2.

3.

2. Memorize your first burst

Know your first two or three sentences like the back of your hand. Be absolutely familiar with your introductory story, fact, Scripture, questions, or quote. If you can ensure that you will get off to a good start, that momentum will often carry throughout your message.

Reflect and Respond ...

Develop strategies that can help you memorize. See if you can make a list of things you can do to memorize. For example, one thing you might do is to repeat your opening remarks several times with someone listening to you for correction and encouragement. What other things might you do? For example, you might memorize short statements.

3. Speak to friendly eyes

There is something comforting in those non-verbal forms of communication (such as eye contact) that let you know people are following you. Note the "eyes that are interested." As you begin, focus on these eyes as you gain a level of comfort and direction.

Reflect and Respond ...

What other non-verbal forms of communication have you observed when you are talking to someone? Identify some and look for them when you are up front at a campus meeting or in church. You can list some of them here.

1.

2.

3.

4.

4. Dress appropriately

It's subtle, but if I travel and speak somewhere that I am completely overdressed for, or underdressed for, I have this tiny nagging discomfort that distracts me from my purpose.

Reflect and Respond ...

What things can you do to ensure that you will be dressed for success when you speak before a group of people you do not know? One simple thing is to find out what the dress attire will be like. What else? Name two or three things you might do.

1.

2.

5. Breathe Deeply!

Take deep breaths just before you begin. Doing this will help to calm you. Focus your mind on the needs of the people and how this message will address those needs.

Reflect and Respond ...

What other calming tactics can you employ to help you right before you speak? Discover what is important and what helps you and do it. Share some of these important things. Write them here in the space provided, or use another sheet of paper.

6. Visualize yourself being effective

See with the eyes of faith. Jesus said to pray for what we desire, not for what we don't desire. This means that we must see ourselves as being used by God. Talk to yourself just before you begin your message, and remind yourself how important this message is.

> "Adam was the only man who, when he said something good, that nobody had said it before him."
> —Mark Twain

Observe other students who are speaking to discover what things you can do to help see yourself being used by God on your campus. For example, memorize Scripture that speaks of God's ability to use you, or write out a prayer asking God to work through you. What else?

7. Wear comfortable clothing

Remove any physical distraction that would hinder you from freely communicating the message. Be sure that you will be relaxed and comfortable. As mentioned earlier, this often depends on the audience you have and where the meeting is held. If you are in the BCM center, one type of dress is appropriate. If you are speaking before Congress, another type of dress might be expected. Learn to be comfortable in both.

Reflect and Respond ...

Besides wearing comfortable clothing, specify two or three ways how you can be certain that you will be as comfortable as possible when you are speaking.

1.

2.

8. Use visual aids

Using visual aids will help take some of the attention off yourself. Sometimes this means going beyond using a film clip using a DVD or VCR. It may mean drawing their attention to an object on a table in the room or even another person, as you collect yourself.

Reflect and Respond ...

Think about visual aids you have seen speakers use that have been helpful in communicating their point. You may have observed these at the BCM or at church. Have you seen PowerPoint used? What are the visual aids you would use in your presentation on campus or at church?

Group Up
What other personal things help you? (For example, walking, singing, sitting, and so forth)

9. Arrive early

There is nothing worse than arriving late to your speaking engagement and finding that things are not set up as you requested. If possible, get to the room at least fifteen minutes early for any last-minute preparations to ensure that the enemy won't divert you with some catastrophe five minutes before you go on.

Reflect and Respond ...

What will help you arrive at your destination on time? For example, does it mean that you will have to leave your college residence earlier than you normally do? Just to go to church is one thing. To be leading a Bible study class is another. Think out a game plan taking into account many of the possible scenarios when you prepare for a speaking engagement.

10. Pray

Obviously, this is the ultimate anxiety solution. Once you've identified the hindrances to reaching your objective, lean on the Holy Spirit for grace and power, and cast over onto God the weight of being responsible to transform lives. This can be done before you speak, as you are speaking, and when you are done.

Reflect and Respond ...

Look up these Scriptures. List beside each one how the truth found in that passage can help you pray and be less anxious before you speak.

Philippians 4:6-7 _____

Hebrews 12:1-2 _____

1 Peter 5:7 _____

Meditate on these passages if or when you become anxious. What other verses might help you when you are anxious? To find other Scripture you might use a biblical concordance. You may have a word search in the back of your Bible that you can use.

Real Life

I met a man who fought in World War II and participated in the D-Day invasion in France, where so many American troops lost their lives. When I asked him about it, he said it was the scariest time of his life. But then he said, "What enabled us to do it was a visit by Winston Churchill, the prime minister of England. He drove up and got out to shake hands with the young soldiers. After meeting us, he stood in the seat of his vehicle and made a five-minute

> Once you've identified the hindrances to reaching your objective, lean on the Holy Spirit for grace and power, and cast over onto God the weight of being responsible to transform lives.

speech that stirred our hearts. He recalled his own fears when he fought in past battles. He spoke of the triumphs that made the effort all worth it. Then he said, 'But gentlemen, that was my hour. This is yours. The fate of the free world now rests on your shoulders. May you fight in such a way as to make your country proud. May this be your finest hour.'"

Churchill knew how to communicate for impact. He lit a flame inside those soldiers that enabled them to accomplish their goal. He knew the secret of speaking the language of leadership.

THE FIVE SECRETS OF SPEAKING THE LANGUAGE OF LEADERSHIP

In his book, *The Sir Winston Method,* James C. Hume summarizes the methods of history's great speakers and communicators such as Benjamin Disraeli, Abraham Lincoln, William Pitt, Franklin D. Roosevelt, and Ronald Reagan.[5] But he zeroes in on Sir Winston Churchill. Churchill exhausted himself in the study of how to communicate to persuade. Or, in Humes' words, how to speak the language of leadership. Here are the five secrets of speaking the language of leadership that Hume explains in his book.

Five Rules ...

Rule 1: Strong beginning
Don't waste time with preliminaries such as, "It's an honor to speak to…" or "I wish to thank…" Praise in the beginning of the speech in front of other students comes off as flattery; the same praise in the middle of the speech comes off as sincerity. You have the greatest attention of the audience right after the introduction. Fill it with something that will grab them. Hit them with an opening zinger like:

- **The Five-Star General**—Use a quotation from someone who commands respect and attention. Keep it short. It only needs to be long enough to make the point.
- **The Sensation Saga**—Begin with a believe-it-or-not case history that relates to your topic or with a story from your own experience. Hook the audience by painting a detailed picture that the audience can imagine.
- **The Paper Ploy**—Comb the newspapers for an offbeat story or sharp quotation that can launch your talk.
- **The Zinger Beginner**—Invent your own quotable line or zinger. Aim for shock or humor impact.

Whichever one of these opening tactics you use, be sure you have a strong beginning that will grab your audience's attention, not send them off daydreaming.

Rule 2: One theme
"A speech is like a symphony. It can have three movements, but it must have one dominant melody." Whenever you speak, know the dominant melody. Know what your problem is. What is the message you want the audience to take away with them? You need to identify your theme and then stick to it. Don't ramble from point to point. Tie up the points into one theme. Remember Martin Luther King, Jr.'s famous speech? It had one theme: "I have a dream." Here are tips for writing a one-theme speech.

- **Statement of bottom-line message**—Before you write out notes for a talk, write out your central theme.
- **Quotation**—Pick a quotation that reinforces one theme.
- **Umbrella**—If you have two or three different points, work up an "umbrella" word or phrase that covers all of them.

"But I tell you that men will have to give account on the day of judgment for every careless word they have spoken. For by your words you will be acquitted and by your words you will be condemned" (Matt. 12:36-37).

- **Anecdote**—Find a story (whether from your own personal experience or one you dug up) that describes the central problem or bottom-line message.
- **Repetition**—Repeat, at least once, the bottom-line message or central theme.
- **Ending**—Be certain the bottom-line message is in your closing.

Rule 3: Simple language

A speech should sound like the way you talk, not like some term paper you once wrote or an article you recently read. The language of leadership is simple language. You use it everyday in common language on campus. Toss out the beat-around-the-bush jargon and use colorful, personal language. Ways to do this include:

- **Pontifical terms**—Throw out the pompous language like "therefore," "however," and "nevertheless," and use the one syllable equivalents: "so," "but," and "still."
- **Is it not romantic?**—Frank Sinatra did not sing it like this, but as "Isn't it romantic?" Like songwriters, speakers ought to use contractions. Contractions are conversational. The more conversational your speech, the more simple it will seem.
- **Get personal**—If you want to persuade your listeners, talk *to* them, not *at* them. Use the personal pronouns *we* and *you*.
- **Best words are the shortest.** Use words that are short, to the point, and that everyone can understand.

Rule 4: Pictures

Do not speak in abstractions. To Churchill "abstractions" were shapeless words that go in one ear and out the other because they don't paint a picture in the listener's mind. And as previously stated, people think in pictures. Get them to connect with your point through pictures. Here are some ways to do this.

- **Paint a picture**—As you speak use your vocabulary to describe a concept or idea that helps other students and non-students visualize it in their minds.

- **Use a story**—Christ used the words *salvation, grace,* and *redemption* in His talks through the use of stories. He talked about a young man who blew all his money on wine, women, and song, then came back and said, "Dad, give me a second chance." To get your point across, use a story. Jesus did.

- **Establish your IRAs**—*IRA* stands for "incident recorded accounts." Each of us have numerous stories from our lives that would translate as a good illustration for a point. Think back and draw from your own life experiences!

- **Take a hike**—If you're stuck and can't think of the right analogy, take a walk. Woods, mountains, or a walk around the block can all suggest ideas.

Rule 5: Emotional ending

"This was their finest hour." Pride in country—that's how Churchill fueled the resolve of Britons during WW II. It is not reason, but passion that stirs the ear. People are emotional creatures and need to be engaged on an emotional level to be moved into action. Some ideas:

- **Vision as a force**—Hope is a powerful emotion. And what is hope but a dream for the future? In talking, you can close by spelling out what the future will hold.
- **You've gotta have a heart**—The language of leadership is the language of the heart. Think of stories or experiences in your own life that moved you close to tears, or made your heart swell with emotion. Close your speech with a poignant personal story that will leave your audience with the full impact of your message on an emotional level.

Group Up
Can you remember a picture of someone painted in your mind? It might be that last lecture you attended or a Bible study you enjoyed. What was it?

Father,
You are the Lord of
communication. You
are the one who puts
words in our mouths.
Help me to
implement the things
in this lesson so that I
may increase Your
kingdom on campus,
in my church, and
wherever I might be.
Give me the same
promise that You gave
to Moses. Be with my
mouth, and teach me
what to say. I know
that You have been
given all power and
authority, which
means Your message
on my lips is Your
powering my life.
Please don't let me
ever forget that.

Amen.

• **Masters of the written word**—If you find it hard to express those feelings from the heart, borrow from a songwriter, or better yet, a poet. They are a good source if you are looking for a good emotional ending.

Access Yourself:

What concepts or ideas have you learned about yourself as a communicator because of this session? List some of them in the space provided. These are for your eyes only.

Think of some areas in which you have room for growth. Again, jot them down in the space provided. These are for your eyes only.

Application

Leadership is influence. Your influence now on campus and in the future is directly proportional to how well you can communicate with those around you. So you can see that your leadership potential is based on how well you seek to communicate your ideas with others.

The best way to become a great communicator is to begin speaking. Take advantage of every opportunity you have to practice the skills and lessons learned in this chapter. You may start off by simply helping make announcements at your BCM. You may lead a prayer in your Bible study group. It is great to know how to communicate, but such knowledge is wasted if it is not put into practice. Write down three opportunities to speak that you will commit to pursuing within the next six months.

1.

2.

3.

Empowering Others

LEARNING HOW LEADERS MULTIPLY THEIR RESULTS

"I cannot carry all these people by myself; the burden is too heavy for me ... The LORD said to Moses: 'Bring me seventy of Israel's elders who are known to you as leaders and officials among the people. Have them come to the Tent of Meeting, that they may stand there with you.' "
—Numbers 11:14,16

"And the things you have heard me say in the presence of many witnesses entrust to reliable men who will also be qualified to teach others."
—2 Timothy 2:2

One of the first movies to come out in the twenty-first century was "Pay It Forward." It vividly depicts the world of the new millennial generation. In it a middle-school teacher challenges his social studies class to do one thing that would "change the world." One student, Trevor McKinney, takes him seriously. He rides his bike down to the dump and picks up a homeless man. After bringing him home for food and sleep, the poor man tries to thank him. Trevor tells him to just go out and help three other people in need. Then those three are given the same instructions, and so on. By the end of the movie, "Pay It Forward" is no longer a class project, it is a movement.

This movie is a great picture of empowerment. What would happen in your Bible study team if suddenly instead of just delegating your work, you made a commitment to also develop each team member as well? Like "Pay It Forward" we would multiply leaders instead of just adding followers. In this lesson, we will examine the progression from merely dumping work on someone else, to delegating work to someone else, to ultimately developing someone else to take on the work—again and again. My goal is to help you move from **addition** to **multiplication** in your leadership.

When ministers (and even students such as yourselves) decide to become leaders, they cross an important line; they make a revolutionary decision on the way to performing their ministry. They are no longer judged only by what they can do themselves. Their value now depends mainly on what they can get done through others! This is what I call "The Jethro Principle."

Do you remember Moses' story? God had led the people of Israel into the wilderness and Moses was acting as the judge over every problem the people had. It all became clear to God's people when Moses' father-in-law, Jethro, saw him attempting to lead the entire nation of Israel all by himself. Jethro basically said to Moses, "The thing that you are doing is not good. You will surely wear out, both yourself and these people who are with you, for the task is too heavy for you; you cannot do it alone. Now listen to me: I shall give you counsel, and God be with you…" So Moses listened to his father-in-law, and did all that he had said (see Ex. 18:19-24).

It All Starts with Change

We will all change. Whether by initiative or by reaction, we will change. Moses was the leader of over 600,000 men—not to mention all the women and children. When Jethro came to visit him, he recognized that burnout was on the horizon for Moses and frustration was on the horizon for the people if Moses continued to do it all himself alone. Jethro saw that Moses needed to change or the result could be disastrous. He pulled his son-in-law aside and spoke to him about his observations. This conversation prompted change in Moses.

Moses made two major changes:
  First, Moses changed his way of thinking.
  Second, Moses changed his way of working.

Here are some actions Moses took to become a leader who would last:

1. He became a man of prayer.
"Listen now to me and I will give you advice, and may God be with you. You must be the people's representative before God and bring their disputes to him" (Ex. 18:19).

Jethro recognized that a leader first needs to be a person of prayer, an intercessor for the people. His first piece of advice to Moses was that he PRAY—pray for the people and for the issues they faced. Without a strong commitment to prayer, a leader will flounder in his or her ability to make prudent decisions and offer wise counsel.

2. He committed himself to communication.
"Teach them the decrees and laws" (v. 20).

Communication is key to effectively leading others. People won't know how to follow unless they are told what they need to do. Communication is the link between ideas and progress.

3. He presented the vision.
"Show them the way to live" (v. 20).

Good leaders always keep the big picture in mind and share it with their followers. They help people see the future toward which they are headed. Moses cast a vision for the way he planned to get things done. He shared the idea of how he would share the leadership load.

4. He developed a plan.
"Show them ... the duties they are to perform" (v. 20).

You can't just stop at sharing the vision—you must come up with a way to get there. If you don't know this, then find Jethro. Jethro impressed on Moses that to be a leader who flourishes, he must develop a plan of action that they would all carry out.

5. He selected and trained the leaders.
"Select capable men from all the people—men who fear God, trustworthy men who hate dishonest gain—and appoint them as officials over thousands, hundreds, fifties and tens" (v. 21).

Jethro must have observed that there were tremendous untapped gifts among the people, because he told Moses to choose leaders from among them and they could handle the majority of the disputes to be settled. He saw the talent and resources available, and utilized them. Notice that their gifts determined the scope of their responsibility; some led thousands, some led tens.

"It is only in developing others that we truly succeed."
—Harvey Firestone

6. He released them to serve according to their gifts.
"Have them serve as judges for the people at all times…the simple cases they can decide themselves" (v. 22).

Once a leader identifies the gifts in a person, he or she must then help them recognize their gifts and encourage them to use them. Jethro encouraged Moses to empower those qualified to judge with the authority and freedom to do so.

7. He only did what they could not do.
"Have them bring every difficult case to you" (v. 22).

Jethro told Moses that he only needed to handle the disputes that they could not, thus freeing up Moses to focus on the bigger matters.

By selecting and preparing "elders" to whom he could delegate smaller leadership matters, Moses was left with more time and energy to give to the larger matters. Jethro saw that Moses could never get the job done the way he was doing it. Fortunately, Jethro's insight and Moses' willingness to change enabled everyone to win.

Reflect and Respond ...

Do you have a "Moses" style of leadership? Would Jethro need to take you aside and have this conversation with you? From the list above, reflect on and list the areas you need to work on.

From Minister to Leader

There is a difference between a minister and a leader. While every leader is also to be a minister, not every minister is a leader. Look at how they differ:

Minister	Leader
1. Serves people	1. Serves people
2. The goal is to meet needs	2. The goal is to empower others to meet the needs
3. Draws fulfillment from doing the work	3. Draws fulfillment from equipping others to do the work
4. Plays defense	4. Plays offense
5. Reacts to needs that arise	5. Creates opportunity to mentor others
6. Immediate-need focus	6. Long-term focus and vision
7. Shepherds others	7. Equips others

Do the things ...
As a collegiate leader, you will need to ...

Do the things that others are unwilling to do:
Servanthood
Do the things that others should do:
Model
Do the things that others can learn to do:
Equip
Do the things that others cannot do:
Lead

Group Up
What steps do you need to take to become a collegiate leader and a minister? Do your steps line up with the four "Do the things"? Discuss it with your group.

Real Life

During the 19th century, a clergyman named Charles Simeon was fed up with the apathetic and liberal men who were filling the pulpits of the Anglican Church in Great Britain. So he decided to do something about it. He took a parish next to Oxford University and created four levels of mentoring groups in a college setting.

First, he spoke in chapel as often as the administration would let him. This exposure introduced him to the entire student body, where he could share his ideas on following Christ as a radical disciple. During these chapels, he would invite students to attend regular meetings he led called "Conversation Groups."

The conversation groups were a **second** level of discipleship for Simeon to invest in the students. He would open it up as a forum, and discuss pertinent issues to the students on how they could become more radical servants of Christ.

Third, from these groups, he would select students who showed promise for ministry to be a part of his "Supper Clubs." These supper meetings took place at his home every week, where he poured into his hand-picked students, preparing them for ministry.

Fourth and finally, from these supper meetings, he would spend special time with an "inner circle" of students who were almost ready to graduate. This group received special time and preparation, as he developed them in leadership for the task ahead.

During his day, the Anglican Church had an unusual practice. The wealthy people in each parish were allowed to control who would fill the pulpits by purchasing them. They would put up the money to pay the clergy; therefore they could decide who they wanted to be their preacher. Consequently, Charles Simeon began to raise money so that he could outbid the rich folks in those parishes, and put one of his young leaders in those leadership positions. He was successful, and impacted the Anglican Church during that century. By his death, a third of the Anglican pulpits were filled with evangelicals he had trained. I have seen the same in BCM life and other college ministries around the United States.[1]

Results of Moses' Change

Once Jethro finished instructing Moses on the changes he needed to make in his leadership, he spoke these words:

> "If you do this and God so commands, you will be able to stand the strain,
> and all these people will go home satisfied" (Ex. 18:23).

The promised result Moses was given if he made these changes was strength for himself and peace for the people. And doesn't that make sense? By releasing some of the burden of leadership to other qualified leaders, Moses was able to keep himself from burnout. And the people experienced peace in being led in an efficient and timely fashion.

Why Do Leaders Fail to Equip?

If this is the promise that comes with equipping others to lead, why do so many leaders keep trying to do it all on their own? Here are some reasons:

"It is better to train a hundred men than to do the work of a hundred men. But it is harder."
—D.L. Moody

- Some realize that equipping people is hard work.
- Some are insecure or have a poor self-image.
- Some feel they are the only one qualified to do it.
- Some don't trust others.
- Some have bad habits and an unbiblical perspective.
- Some have a low belief in people.
- Some don't know how to train others.
- It is easier to lead followers than leaders.

Equipping others takes energy, time, and careful planning, especially during collegiate years as you develop your leadership style. It is a proactive way of leading, rather than the way many leaders unfortunately run their organizations. It means that, as a leader, you will need to allow others ownership of the work you are doing. This requires a belief and trust in others and the ability to relinquish control. However, if you commit to equipping people as a leader, you will find Jethro's promises to be true in your life and leadership. One campus program attributes its longevity and success to "students leading students." How is your campus program run?

Reflect and Respond ...

Honestly evaluate yourself against the previous list. Do you see any of the reasons given present in you as a leader? Jot them down so you won't forget.

As a leader, what are some steps you will commit to take to move away from doing things on your own toward equipping others? These are really important. Jot down several and stick to them. If you are in a CrossSeekers or some other form of Covenant group, ask others in the group to hold you accountable to these things you are listing.

Group Up
Have you seen collegiate leaders who were unwilling to equip? What was the result in most cases?

A Leader's Math Skills

Collegiate leaders who develop leaders multiply. Unfortunately, some leaders can only seem to do addition. They are focused on getting followers, not developing leaders. Having followers isn't necessarily bad, but if you want to have any exponential impact on the kingdom of God, you need to practice your multiplication. Which have you observed in your collegiate friends on campus or in the church?

Followers Math = Addition   **Leaders Math = Multiplication**[2]

As a college leader you must be good at math. You must not be satisfied with addition. You should seek to multiply the leadership of others.

Differences between leaders who develop leaders and leaders who develop followers

1. Desire
   Leaders who develop Followers NEED TO BE NEEDED.
   Leaders who develop Leaders WANT TO BE SUCCEEDED.

2. Focus

Leaders who develop Followers FOCUS ON THE WEAKNESS OF PEOPLE.
Leaders who develop Leaders FOCUS ON THE STRENGTHS OF PEOPLE.

3. Priorities

Leaders who develop Followers DEVOTE ATTENTION TO THE BOTTOM 20 PERCENT.
Leaders who develop Leaders DEVOTE ATTENTION TO THE TOP 20 PERCENT.

4. Abilities

Leaders who develop Followers ARE GOOD LEADERS.
Leaders who develop Leaders ARE GREAT LEADERS.

5. Attitude

Leaders who develop Followers LIFT UP THEMSELVES.
Leaders who develop Leaders LIFT UP OTHERS.

6. Time

Leaders who develop Followers SPEND TIME WITH PEOPLE.
Leaders who develop Leaders INVEST TIME IN PEOPLE.

7. Expectations

Leaders who develop Followers ASK FOR LITTLE COMMITMENT.
Leaders who develop Leaders ASK FOR MUCH COMMITMENT.

8. Leadership

Leaders who develop Followers LEAD EVERYONE THE SAME.
Leaders who develop Leaders LEAD EVERYONE DIFFERENTLY.

9. Impact

Leaders who develop Followers IMPACT THIS GENERATION.
Leaders who develop Leaders IMPACT THE NEXT GENERATION.[3]

How I Learned This Truth

I became a pastor in 1979. After four years, I made a radical shift in how I led the people God gave me. Up to that point, I was like Moses in Exodus 18. I was doing all the work. I was the speaker. I planned the social events. I led the mid-week Bible study. I made the posters and promotional flyers. I even set up the chairs and platform in our meeting room. Everyone came to me when they needed anything. I had all the power, but unfortunately, I also had all the responsibility. Boy, was I tired every week!

In 1983, I changed. It was like I had a little talk with Jethro. I began to invest a majority of my time selecting leaders and workers, and developing them. For example, I noticed we had a shortage of male leaders in our college group, so I started a mentoring a group of seven men in order to build leaders. Each of them had to meet two criteria. First, they were to take on a leadership position. Second, they were to reproduce their leadership in someone else when our group finished.

I delegated leadership of the ministry teams to 11 people. I turned college students loose to disciple other college students and lead small groups. I found graphic artists within the group to take on the task of promoting events. In fact, I matched ministry tasks with students and non-students who had spiritual gifts for those jobs. It was awesome. Surprisingly, I was more fulfilled coaching and cheering on my team of leaders than I was doing it all myself.

"I begin with the premise that the goal of leadership is to build more leaders."
—Ralph Nader

The result? My department averaged about 60 people in 1983. Within seven years, we averaged about 600 people. More than half of them had a regular volunteer ministry. And we had more than 60 leaders who had positions of leadership. I was merely the coach who equipped them and cheered them on!

Reflect and Respond ...

Think about and jot down in the space provided one word to describe what kind of leader you naturally tend to be.

Who are you developing to be a leader in your campus group or in church?

What prevents you from developing others more effectively? What steps do you need to take to improve immediately?

Sharing the Work with Others

"He is the one who gave these gifts to the church, the apostles, the prophets, the evangelists, and the pastors and teachers. Their responsibility is to equip God's people to do his work and build up the church, the body of Christ" (Eph. 4:11-12).

In Ephesians 4:11-12, what did Paul say is our responsibility as leaders?

What results as we equip the people of God?

Because the Scripture calls us to share our ministry with others, it is important that we understand how to do this well. First, let me point out that there are three levels of shared ministry:

Dumping
This method is when you simply dump a task into the hands of another student, or even your campus leader. You are relieved that it is no longer your responsibility, but usually fail to understand the damage you do to that person you've dumped on.

Delegating
This style is when you plan ahead and think through how you will pass on a task to someone else. No damage is done this way, but the focus is still on eliminating a task, not developing a person.

Developing
This method is the ultimate way to share a ministry. You plan ahead, prepare the student(s) to take on the task, and the focus is on the training of the student. Both you and the other student win in the end.

Group Up
When someone on campus or in the church did not allow you to have influence in a meeting, how did you react?

The Football Problem

I am sure you have been to a football game. Consider this humorous analogy. Every football game has two components. First, there are 22 players on the field in desperate need of rest. Second, there are 50,000 people in the stands in desperate need of exercise!

This scenario is a picture of most ministries today. For example, let's examine a typical church. Most of the work is done by a few people. This is probably true in your Bible study group. Much of the activity is not shared by the majority. The pastor and the other leaders are not running around, performing 80 percent of the tasks. They are tired. Some are burned out. Sadly, it is unnecessary. The rest of the people are satisfied to sit and watch the show. They are complacent. Some complain. Most of them need spiritual exercise!

I believe leaders need to act more like coaches. They need to train and empower people to be players. Then they need to turn them loose to play the game. The only way they are going to develop into decent players is if they get a little experience, a little playing time. No doubt, leaders will feel they do it better than the students do, at first. But collegiate leaders must begin this transfer of the work if they are going to multiply what gets done.

How to Do It

How do we develop others? Here are some suggestions:

1. **Know yourself.**—Be familiar with the strengths you pass on to others in the work.

2. **Know the person you wish to develop.**—Be familiar with their strengths and weaknesses. Understand their limitations so you don't overwhelm them with too much and help them exercise their areas of giftedness.

3. **Clearly define the assignments and give them responsibilities.**—Don't leave anything to question; write it down. Send an email. This way, neither one of you will have questions about what they are supposed to accomplish.

4. **Teach the "why" behind the assignment.**—Let them know why their assignment is important. Help them understand the reason behind which you are operating.

5. **Discuss their growth process as you go.**—Talk about how they will grow from working with you as a team player. Show them the ways in which they will develop and point out the areas in which they have already grown.

6. **Spend relational time with them.**—Invest time when you are not talking about school or your Bible study group. Become a friend to them, not just an impersonal leader.

7. **Allow them to watch you minister.**—Let them observe you in action and allow them to give feedback to you. Encourage them to email you their impressions after a time together.

8. **Give them the resources they need.**—Provide the tools to do the job. Resource them so they are not questioning where to go or what to do to get the job done. If you do not have the resources, tell them. Then, as a team, see if you can find the resources to get the job done.

9. **Encourage them to journal during the process.**—Help them interpret their growth through writing and processing on paper. Not only will they gain insight from this exercise,

they will have a record of their growth to refer to. Encourage them to obtain a notebook and paper to reserve just for this purpose.

10. Hold them accountable for their ministry.—Get permission from each member of your group or the covenant group to keep them in line.

11. Give them the freedom to fail.—Communicate that they can learn as they go and that you will be there to help if they begin to struggle.

12. Debrief and affirm them regularly.—Encourage them all along the way as they succeed.

Reflect and Respond ...

How many of these 12 suggestions revolve around your leaders-in-training? around you? Is that of significance? ❑ Yes ❑ Not sure ❑ It varies from student to student ❑ Not at all

Put "10s" on Their Foreheads!

John Maxwell practiced a little secret that helped him believe in the people around him. He said he would put an imaginary "10" on their foreheads when he would see them. The number meant that on a scale of 1 to 10, they got a top score. They had potential. They were God's child. They were loaded with gifts. They were special. This way, instead of remembering their past failures and treating them accordingly, he would see them as the most important people he had met that day. Nobody got treated like a "4" or a "5." Everyone got treated like a "10!" I know...I was one of them. You see, Dr. Maxwell taught me that people usually rise to the expectation of the leader. If you treat people as they are, you get only what they have done already. But if you treat them as they could be, you get to see them reach their potential.

Reflect and Respond ...

What have you been doing as a leader?
Dumping? ❑
Delegating? ❑
Developing? ❑
Or some of each? ❑

Review the suggestions on the previous page.
Ask yourself this question: What have you already been doing?

Now ask: What can you do to better empower others?

Group Up
What number is on the forehead of those in your collegiate Bible study group? What number do you feel God see on your head?

It's All About Relationships

Developing people is all about relationships. Think about it. Leadership is relationships! It has everything to do with doing relationships well. If you determine to develop people in your leadership, you will have to become a PROVIDER in your relationships with people. A leader is a "soul provider."

Define It ...
What exactly does it mean to be a provider in relationships? A provider is a spiritual leader. Do you remember the definition we examined earlier? A provider (spiritual leader) is:

One who assumes responsibility for the health and development of their relationships.

Providers Are ...
P – Purposeful—You approach people with a clear goal.

R – Relational—You are warm and approachable with others.

O – Objective—You can see both strengths and weaknesses.

V – Vulnerable—You initiate transparency and openness.

I – Incarnational—You model the qualities they hope to pass along.

D – Dependable—You are committed to others along the way.

E – Empowering—You give away your power to people.

R – Resourceful—They harness their tools and use them strategically.

"The Law of Reproduction: It takes a leader to raise up a leader."
—John Maxwell

Reflect and Respond ...

Are you a provider for others? In what areas are you weak or strong? List them below.

Weak	Strong

Jesus' Idea

Since our goal in delegation should be to develop people, it is imperative for us to understand how change is best fostered in people. When we turn to the pages of Scripture, we find the ideal model to follow is Jesus, the Master-mentor.

We can summarize how Jesus brought about life change by taking the word "IDEA," and allowing it to serve as a reminder of the Hebraic model He employed. The following is how He did it:

I – Instruction in a life-related context

He took time to teach and instruct them verbally.

D – Demonstration in a life-related context

He modeled truths and let the disciples observe it.

E – Experience in a life-related context

He let the disciples participate and apply truth themselves.

A – Accountability in a life-related context

He debriefed their shared experience and assessed their growth.

Reflect and Respond ...

Reflect on some of the stories from Jesus' life and leadership. Name at least one example of how He practiced each of the four elements of this IDEA. Can you do it? (If not, review the Gospels—Matthew, Mark, Luke, and John. Observe Jesus through the eyes of a leader.)

1.
2.
3.
4.

Do you get the "IDEA"? Which portions of this leadership style have you put into practice following Jesus' model of mentoring?

Empowering People

As collegiate spiritual leaders, we begin our journey with some basic skills. Most of us shepherd others naturally. Our challenge is to move from shepherding to equipping, where our interaction with other students prepares them to take on responsibility. However, the highest goal is to move from equipping to developing others. This occurs when leaders focus not only on training others to help with the work, but mentoring and growing them to become better leaders.

Shepherding	Equipping	Developing
Care	Training for ministry	Training for personal growth
Immediate needs	Talk-focus	Person-focus
Focus	Transactional	Transformational
Relational	Management	Leadership
Service	Ministry by addition	Ministry by multiplication
Ministry	Short-term	Long-term
Feeling better	Unleashing	Empowering
Availability	Teaching	Mentoring
Focus on nurture	Focus on specific ministry	Focus on specific leader
No curriculum	Curriculum set	Curriculum flexible
Need-oriented	Skill-oriented	Being
Maintenance	Doing	What do they need?
What is the problem?	What do I need?	Person-focused
Problem-focused	Purpose-focused	**THEY'LL WALK THE SECOND MILE.**
THEY BEGIN TO WALK.	**THEY'LL WALK THE FIRST MILE.**	

Group Up

Who on your campus, in your church, or in your community do you want to walk the second mile? Have you worked through these steps with him or her?

Bringing It All Home

More than 200 years ago, England experienced spiritual revival. Two men played key roles in this revival: George Whitefield and John Wesley. Historians have written that Whitefield was the better preacher. He had been an actor and had a booming voice that could reach thousands of people without amplification. He had a great impact on his generation.

However, historians also agree that Wesley's impact was longer lasting. It stretched beyond his generation. Here's why. As John Wesley saw people coming to Christ, he knew he had to invest in them, if they were to become disciples. He started "class meetings," which were simply small accountability groups. He attempted to organize all his converts into these groups. Soon he realized he could not follow up on everyone, even in the groups, so he began to train lay preachers to ride the circuit on horseback and minister to the converts. He even had chapels built where he could train these lay leaders. Needless to say, a movement began. He was so intentional in his methods of training that contemporaries called him the great "Methodist." The Methodist church got its beginnings from John Wesley and still exists today.[4]

Church history is interesting. Although Whitefield was a more gifted preacher, Wesley was a better leader. One historian wrote that Whitefield's legacy was a "rope of sand," but Wesley's legacy has outlived him by more than 200 years. One started a ministry to his generation. The other started a movement that continues to this day. The same is true for many campus groups, including the Baptist Campus Ministry program that is on over 1,000 campuses sharing the good news of Christ and how to be Christian leaders.

Assess Yourself

What changes in your way of thinking/working should you make to implement Jethro's advice?

After working through this section and evaluating yourself, are you a leader who is developing followers or a leader who develops leaders? Are you practicing
- ❏ addition?   ❏ multiplication?

Think of another student who you can begin developing now as a leader. Write below the steps you will take, starting now, to begin doing this. Commit yourself to being a leader who develops other leaders on your campus and begin to have an impact on generations to come.

Application

We all know that multiplication brings greater results than addition, yet many of us are not willing to take the risk of giving freedom to those who work under us.

Have you ever stopped to think that this freedom greatly resembles the freedom that God gives to us? He gives us freedom to do things our own way, and sometimes that means we do things that are directly against His will. Through these times He teaches and improves us, and in the end we are wiser than before. He knows that even though the risk is great, the returns are far greater. These principles are the same for your ministry as well.

On a separate sheet of paper, write down the names of people you plan to develop and empower to serve. Then … go do it.

Leading an Effective Meeting

7

HOW YOU CAN ORGANIZE AND LEAD A FRUITFUL TEAM MEETING

"Plans fail for lack of counsel, but with many advisers they succeed."
—Proverbs 15:22

An experienced leader once said, "For God so loved the world, that He didn't send a committee ..." It is possible that more leaders have been frustrated by the long, verbose, and ineffective committee meetings they're forced to attend than anything else. For many, it's a burdensome part of their job. A pastor once said, "A meeting is no substitute for progress!"

In 1989, a survey was taken among pastors and church leaders. They were asked the question: "What subject would you most want to read a book about to help you do your job?" Two-thirds of them said: "A book on how to work with boards, committees, and teams." Let's face it. Most of us have never been trained on how to lead a meeting, or what to do to get the most out of the people on your team. It's a foreign subject—and yet it's familiar territory for every leader. What's more, it is critical that every leader know how to do it. Dr. Carl George, from the Fuller Church Growth Institute, said the one behavior that they look for to gauge the influence of a leader is: Can they convene a meeting?[1]

Hmmm. What an interesting evaluation tool for every leader. Do students show up? Does the leader carry weight when he or she speaks? Do they influence the direction of the team? Have they organized the agenda? Who is listening and responding? What gets accomplished?

I Wasn't Ready for This!

Kristen had just taken her position as president of the Baptist Collegiate Ministry program on her campus. She was excited! That is, until she realized that she not only had to lead the weekly BCM meetings for the ministry, but she would have to lead a very diverse and stubborn team that had been elected at the same time. At their first meeting, things got tense, as two individuals dominated the whole meeting. Both were at odds over what they should do for the big fundraiser held during the fall semester. Nothing was accomplished at the meeting. When Kristen spoke with them later about their rude and stubborn behavior, they both felt badly. However, the next meeting was another dismal failure. No one spoke up. Everyone was afraid of hurting someone's feelings. Kristen was at a loss for what to do to make this group of people a team that could get something done.

The good news is this. That's what this chapter is all about.

Basic Truth
Collegiate leaders accomplish goals through organizing people and resources.

Guided Prayer
Father,
I don't have a clue how to lead a meeting!

Everyone on my team has different personalities and agendas, but I know You understand them all.

Give me wisdom on how to meet with my team in the most fruitful way possible.

Amen.

Have you ever led a meeting before? ❑ Yes ❑ No

If you said yes, can you remember what was the best and worst part of your experience? Jot one of each down in the space provided:

Best—

Worst—

Think of some suggestion of what you would do if you were Kristen in the situation above. Give her some advice in the space below.

Four Reasons Why This Chapter Is Important

1. Nothing will affect your collegiate (and beyond) leadership success more than the team/committee with whom you work.

2. Most collegiate leaders have never been trained in how to lead committees or team meetings.

3. Most church leaders have had a negative experience with committee work in the past.

4. Most campus teams or church committees are not as effective as they could be.

> "Committee—a group of people who keep minutes and waste hours."
> —Milton Berle

Setting Up the Meeting

OK, so you're supposed to lead your campus or church team meetings. Are you excited about the potential you have for really getting something accomplished? Are you scared of wasting your team's time? Do you think you've got a strong agenda for the meeting? Let's take a look at some simple steps you can take to set up the meeting for success.

1. Contact each team member personally, and confirm the meeting time and location. Let them know you're excited about them being part of the meeting and you are counting on them to participate. Use email, if possible.

2. Ask all team members to notify you if they cannot attend. An email is sufficient (so long as it's not 10 minutes before the meeting). Make certain they feel accountable for being participants at the meetings and responsible to notify you if they can't hold up their commitment.

3. Schedule the meetings in a comfortable and safe place for discussion. Take initiative in setting the tone and atmosphere for the meeting.

4. Foster participation by asking collegians to prepare a report for the meeting. This insures there's been some forethought going into the meeting and students aren't just "winging it." This is really a help for them, even if they aren't aware of it.

5. Determine beforehand how long and how often the meetings will be. Let's face it. It seems everyone's schedule is busy. Let them know you won't waste their time with needless or lengthy meetings. Determine the commitment up front.

6. Meet with your team members individually outside of the meetings (if possible) to establish relationship and to understand expectations. This will accelerate trust and progress during the meetings, and will enable that person to also be responsible for the meeting.

7. Always invest some time for personal growth and some time for organizational business. Let members know you are interested in them and their personal lives. Take time to develop them as collegiate leaders or disciples. Then go on to the business of the meeting. (You may want to do this in two separate meetings, based on the time constraints you work with.)

A Planning Meeting Should Include:

1. Written conclusion
Write down what you have decided to do.

2. Personal responsibility
It is important that everyone is cooperating to complete the goal. I mentioned earlier "ownership." People develop ownership of a project when they are given responsibility for the completion of a specific area. People support what they help create. Back it up with an email.

3. Timeline
Let everyone know when events are going on. If there are deadlines to be met, it will be important to communicate this to your team. Back it up with an email.

4. Listing of resources
A list will help you gain a realistic view of what you have and what you don't have, including people, talents, computers, money, and time.

5. Next steps
Make a list of the steps you are going to do next in the completion of the goal. Remember, be realistic. Back it up with an email to each member of your team.

6. Person in charge of project
Leadership is key in accomplishing a goal. As a collegiate leader you will have the ability to keep everyone working together as a team and completing the goal.

Meetings That Develop People and Do Business

During the 11 years that I led the collegian department at Skyline Church, we held leadership meetings with our small-group leaders, our council (administrative leaders), and our ministry team leaders. Our department averaged about 600 attendees each week, and I worked with about 65 leaders on a consistent basis. In our meetings, we combined both personal development (equipping) and organizational development (business).

Because we had a diverse group of leaders and positions, I formed an agenda that gave them the big picture for our ministry, and specific time to grow in their individual areas of concern. We met monthly and meetings lasted approximately two hours.

Group Up
As a busy collegian, do you feel you can fill all these roles?
If not, what do you think will help you improve?

"A camel looks like a horse that was planned at a committee meeting."
—anonymous

Our Agenda (A Sample to Examine)

(You develop yours with your team)

1. **Vision time**—This time was for sharing the big-picture vision for what God was doing in our department since we last met. We would use testimonies and share victory stories. This was a time for celebration. (We even gave out huge candy bars to those who shared!)

2. **Administrative time**—This segment was meant to communicate relevant information to each student leader for the whole department: announcements, reminders of upcoming events, and important items to be aware of.

3. **Skill time**—Next, we'd divide up our large group into two parts: Leadership Foundations (those who'd been leaders for less than a year) and Leadership Fitness (those who'd been leaders for one year or more). We'd do appropriate training time with each. One was basic training, the other was advanced training.

4. **Huddle time**—Finally, we'd give them a final 30 minutes to meet with their individual areas, such as small-group leaders, and council and ministry team leaders. In this time, they could concentrate on personal application for campus application or items pertinent to their own ministry area.

Meetings That Develop People

If the purpose of your meeting is simply to coach your team, I suggest the following format, which allows for discussion and personal mentoring. As you consider your goals, remember this acronym for S.A.L.T. It will help you flow in your coaching:

Step	Your Role
S – Say something affirming Always begin with a word of hope and optimism about what God wants to accomplish through your team and this meeting.	**A Host** Hosts take initiative and make others comfortable.
A – Ask the right questions Move to some thought-provoking questions that begin with the end in mind. What must we do to cooperate with God fulfilling His purposes here?	**A Doctor** Doctors poke and prod while seeking a diagnosis.
L – Listen well Always take time to listen and value each person's input. This creates a safe atmosphere to communicate and learn.	**A Counselor** Counselors connect with people by actively listening.
T – Target the discussion Finally, you must guide the discussion to the best conclusions.	**A Tour Guide** Tour guides aren't hired to fellowship but to get folks to a destination.

This means redirecting people away from tangents, back to the ultimate goals of the discussion.

Brainstorming Their Goals

Part of your meeting may include brainstorming or just adjusting each member's goals. Glen Urgulart and Bobb Biehl suggest some ideas when you want to simply discuss reaching each team member's goals. The students should come to the meeting prepared to discuss:

1. A list of one to three upcoming DECISIONS to which the team can give perspective.

2. A list of one to three PROBLEMS in reaching their goals to discuss with the team.

3. A list of PLANS for the team's general information and update.

4. A list of PROGRESS POINTS so the team can give well-deserved praise.

5. A list of PRAYER REQUESTS for the team's prayers and general support.

6. A list of ROAD BLOCKS, blind spots, and fears they would like to discuss.

Reflect and Respond ...

1. Reflect on a past experience. When you would meet to develop or coach someone, how did you approach the task? Jot some thoughts down in the space provided.

After thinking about S.A.L.T., how would you coach someone now? Jot down several ideas in the space provided.

2. What tools or resources could you use to mentor someone in leadership while they are still on your campus? This is a time to brainstorm with the team. What tools do you need?

Meetings That Do Business

If your goal is simply to conduct business for your organization, then a different agenda is in order. Years ago, Olen Hendricks suggested the following order for business/committee meetings. As a Christian student leading meetings other than Bible studies, it is important to read through the agenda categories and see the logic of each one.

1. Information items

The first category on the agenda is "information items." These items are issues that need to be communicated, announced, and reported as victories since the last meeting. By doing this first, you have the attendees when they are fresh to look at their calendars. Also, by reporting the victories since the last meeting, it sets a productive tone for the meeting.

2. Study items

The second category is called "study items." These items are subjects you wish to brainstorm, and "dream out loud" about but aren't yet ready to vote on. Typically, any issue should be a study item once or twice before it comes to the agenda as an item to vote on and take action. These items allow members to talk about future issues without the pressure of having to make an immediate decision.

3. Action items

The final category is called "action items." These items are previous study items from past agendas that are ready for a vote. By the time an issue becomes an action item, there has been plenty of discussion and everyone is familiar with it—now you are ready to act.

Reflect and Respond ...

1. Think about possible issues you might have on a future agenda. Relate them to where they fit in the format above.

Information items:

Study items:

Action items:

2. Which of the three categories do you think would take the most time?

Which category should take the most time?

Eight Principles for Leading Effective Meetings

Dr. John Maxwell offers these principles to keep in mind as you plan to lead team meetings[2]:

1. Understand what undermines good meetings.

    a. Meeting objectives are poorly defined. Put your objectives in print: why exactly are you meeting?

    b. People are invited based on protocol, not need. Invite those who can solve problems, not merely represent needs from the group.

    c. We often hold non-essential meetings. Don't just meet because of tradition. If you don't have a legitimate reason to meet, cancel it.

    d. Participants are not prepared for the meeting. Give team members material ahead of time, so they are ready to discuss issues.

    e. Meetings last too long. The longer a meeting goes, the more attendees lose interest and creativity.

    f. Trying to reach consensus on minor points. Decide what's really worth dying for. Don't waste much time on unimportant issues.

    g. Meeting is held in an atmosphere that's not conducive for discussion. If you're going to talk about sensitive issues, don't meet in a loud or public place.

    h. One person is allowed to dominate the meeting. If this happens, talk to them prior and ask them to speak last and summarize the discussion.

    i. The facilitator of the meeting is not a good leader. This should give you incentive to become a better leader each week!

    j. No action or wrong action is taken after the meeting. Nothing kills meetings more than knowing no (or wrong) action will be taken.

Group Up
As a college student, which one of these points is the most difficult for you to recognize and resolve?

Reflect and Respond ...

1. Have you ever been in a meeting in which the leader (student or non-student) failed to recognize one of these negative issues listed above? Share as much in bullet-form what you remember.

2. In your personal opinion, which issue did the leader fail to recognize? Jot it here.

3. What happened to create the problem in the meeting (if you can identify one or more items)?

2. Know how to handle difficult people in the meeting.
This de-motivates everyone present. Here are some common difficult personalities:

  a. **The Eager Beaver**—They jump in to talk and summarize the topic immediately.
     Solution: You should ask them to summarize the discussion at the end.

  b. **The Obstinate Person**—They are stubborn and opinionated.
     Solution: You should ask others to comment on their opinion to balance the issue.

  c. **The Dampener**—They are negative and can't see solutions.
     Solution: You should ask them, "What would you do to solve this problem?"

  d. **The Indiscriminating**—They agree with every suggestion and idea.
     Solution: You should acknowledge their words, but keep the discussion moving.

  e. **Silent Sam**—Their silence appears to be a disagreement or hidden agenda.
     Solution: Sit next to them and continue to ask, "What do you think about this idea?"

  f. **The Inattentive**—They are present in body but not in mind.
     Solution: Ask them a specific question to bring them back into the discussion.

  g. **The Griper**—They waste time always complaining.
     Solution: Communicate the time deadline before they begin speaking.

  h. **The Highly Argumentative Person**—They want to argue over everything.
     Solution: Always ask their opinion first so they can't disagree with anyone.

  i. **The Inarticulate Person**—They have a difficult time expressing their thoughts.
     Solution: Let them talk, then review and repeat what you think they said.

  j. **The Side Conversationalist**—They have extra conversations during the meeting.
     Solution: When they do this, call them by name and ask them a question.

  k. **The Rambler**—They talk on every subject except the one being discussed.
     Solution: When they stop for a breath, jump in and refocus on the subject at hand.

  l. **The Late Attendee**—They always show up late to the meeting.
     Solution: Call them before the meeting and ask them to open the meeting in prayer.

3. Allow no hidden agendas.
When people bring hidden agendas to a meeting, don't bring them up until the end. It can really hinder the progress and morale of a team. Unless it's an emergency, let your team know they must communicate agenda items to you before the meeting. This way, no one subverts the direction of the meeting because of some special interest group or selfish agenda. Here are just some of the reasons why hidden agendas can be negative:

Group Up
Do you have students such as these in your group?

Which one are you? If you have to pick more than one, circle each one that is a part of you.

a. Your team members aren't prepared to discuss and act on it.

b. The student bringing it up often represents others who don't see the big picture.

c. The hidden agenda is often based on a wrong motive.

4. Have an agenda that works *for* you and not *against* you.

Some examples of these have already been given. You first need to determine: what is the purpose of this meeting? Note the summary below:

AGENDAS FOR BUSINESS MEETINGS:	AGENDAS FOR COACHING MEETINGS:	AGENDAS THAT ACCOMPLISH BOTH:
a. Information items b. Study items c. Action items	S—Say something affirming *(You are a host.)* A—Ask the right questions *(You are a doctor.)* L—Listen well *(You are a counselor.)* T—Target the discussion *(You are a tour guide.)* (At this point, you lead the discussion on a growth area for the team.)	a. Vision Time (20 min.) b. Administrative Time (20 min.) c. Break (20 min.) d. Skill Time (30 min.) e. Huddle Time (30 min.)

5. Understand your role with the team.

This is key for you as a college student discovering new ways to live out your life. To understand this aspect of Christian leadership is vital for future success. There are three vital roles. Are you expected to be the director—a leader who gives direction to the team and the organization? Or are you supposed to be a representative of the people—only acting on their wishes, since they voted you into office? Are you expected to be a sort of chaplain—simply caring for the people but not really acting as a change agent?

One role (the director) allows you to spearhead the decision-making process. The other two (the representative and chaplain roles) do not. What are the expectations and boundaries of the role you are to play? Here is what you should do, depending on your role:

If you are a DIRECTOR, bring an agenda to the meeting and direct it.

If you are a REPRESENTATIVE, bring a notepad and take notes.

If you are a CHAPLAIN, bring your Bible and provide spiritual support.

Next, you must help your leadership team understand their roles in the organization. Do other students expect them to meet as "directors" or as "representatives"? This is the dilemma facing many politicians today in Washington, D.C. Some see themselves as leaders. They figure the people voted them in because they trusted them to lead and make the best decisions for their country or state. Others see themselves as representatives. They are to listen and carry out the wishes of the special interest groups of their constituency. If the people expect one thing and the politician expects another—there will be trouble.

> "One reason the Ten Commandments are so short and to the point is the fact that they were given direct, and did not come out of an ethics committee!"
> —H. G. Hutcheson

Great Expectations

Todd was elected as president of his SGA (student government association). He was excited until he showed up at the first officer's meeting. He came ready to lead the meeting and engineer positive changes to the campus. Unfortunately, the officers came with dozens of different agendas. What's worse, the variety of agenda issues weren't necessarily from the officers themselves. The officers brought them from a myriad of special interest groups on campus. One group wanted this, another group wanted that. It was chaos.

Needless to say—the meeting lasted extremely long. When it was over, few left satisfied, and no one left feeling fulfilled. There was a fight over which special interest group had a louder voice. Afterward, Todd realized his problem. He had one expectation of his role, and his officers had a very different one. At his next meeting, Todd invested an hour discussing what the role of the SGA was to be. When everyone saw the reason for the confusion at the last meeting, and agreed upon a course of action, they were free to work together for the first time.

In a Christian ministry or organization, you will very likely face the same problem. For you, the central leadership question is this: are you to listen to God and carry out what you believe He is directing you to do, or are you to listen to the people (trusting that they will communicate the Lord's will) and carry out what they say to do?

Reflect and Respond ...

1. Examine your role in your campus or church group. If you are in a leadership role, what's your expectation of your role? You may want to go back and examine the three roles. In the space below, write in some expectations.

What do the people in your group expect from you? Again, in the space below, write in some expectation other people in your group expect from you.

2. Think specifically about one leadership group. Do your team leaders in this specific role fulfill the expectations of your group as a whole? Why or why not?

"Your goal should not be to build big organizations, but to build big people."
—John Maxwell

6. Invest time developing your team in spiritual and leadership growth.

In addition to accomplishing the tasks you have been given, you must invest time growing together. As leaders, you will only lead others as far as you have grown yourself. In fact, you cannot lead anyone beyond where you have gone as a leader. Consequently, you must plan times to meet for personal growth as a group, not just business. Some ideas might be:

    a. A spiritual leadership retreat near the beginning of the year

    b. A monthly time to meet for spiritual leadership training, prayer, and discussion

    c. Personal mentoring time between you as the leader and your team members

Have you ever stopped to evaluate Jesus' leadership style? He had two important objectives when He came to earth. First, to get to the cross. Second, to equip twelve leaders. There are others, of course, but we want to concentrate on these two.

Robert Coleman, in his excellent book, *The Master Plan of Evangelism,* reminds us of Jesus' style of leadership development. Frequently, Jesus would take His team of twelve far away from the crowds for training. Jesus spent so much time with these twelve, in comparison to the masses, that it can only be interpreted as a deliberate strategy. He actually spent more time with His twelve disciples than He spent with everyone else in the world put together! It might do us good to follow the leadership model of Jesus.

Jesus and the 80/20 Principle

Jesus implemented the 80/20 Principle. He probably spent 80 percent of His time with about 20 percent of His key people. This enabled Him to develop them as leaders—who would change the world within a generation! (see Acts 17:6 and 19:10). He was multiplying His leadership, not merely adding to the kingdom by doing all the leadership Himself.

Consider this: Jesus taught His team of twelve exclusively. The Sermon on the Mount was likely directed to His small band of disciples (Matt. 5:1). He performed a number of miracles in the presence of His twelve, and no more. Remember the calming of the storm? How about the time He invited Peter to walk on the water? Further, Jesus invited three of His twelve on exclusive ministry engagements, where no one else was invited to go. Only Peter, James, and John went up on the Mount of Transfiguration (Matt. 17:1); only Peter, James, and John were invited in to see Jesus raise Jairus's daughter from the dead (Mark 5:37). And Peter, James, and John were asked to come apart and pray with Him in the garden of Gethsemane (Matt. 26:36-37). Jesus spent time doing special training of His key leaders. So should we.

An Idea

One idea you could easily employ is to use as guides this book, or others in this series, such as *Authentic Influence: Leading Without Titles.* Put a copy into the hands of each team member, and plan to journal and discuss a chapter weekly, or every other week, or perhaps even once a month. The point is—you must invest time developing your team. If they are forced to keep giving, without any input into their own lives, eventually they will either tire out or burn out.

Imagine the results if all your leadership were trained.

Ways to order *Authentic Influence* can be found on the back of the inside title page.

Group Up
As a spiritual leader on campus, what are some ideas that your team can do for personal leadership growth as Christians?

Brainstorm with your group.

"Sometimes a committee is a thing which takes a week to do what one good man can do in one hour."
—Elbert Hubbard

Assess Yourself

What did your last meeting look like?

_____

Poor   OK   Good/Effective

Can you identify why you gave it the score you did?

In light of this chapter, as a Christian leader on your campus or at church, think of three things you will change to make your next meeting a "10."

1.

2.

3.

Application

As we talked about earlier, we need to invest in the lives of those who work with us. This is crucial in covenant living. It is one of the best feelings in the world to know that you are part of a team that cares for you. It's great when they hold you accountable for Christian living and leadership. On the other hand, it is one of the worst feelings when you believe that what you do has no impact. It's almost as though no one cares. It might seem your Christian leadership is having no impact. Not true! However, let those around you know that you are looking out for them and that you care about them. Choose an agenda from this chapter that best fits your goals. Then use it at your next meeting.

Steps to Building a Great Meeting

Using ideas you have gleaned from the book thus far, list the major principles you want to use in being the leader God wants you to be on campus. The list can fill this page and the next, or it might only be two or three points. This action almost becomes the first step in journaling yourself into leadership on campus.

Leading When You'd Rather Be Leaving

DEALING WITH DIFFICULT PEOPLE AND DRAINING POSITIONS

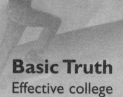

"Consider it pure joy, my brothers, whenever you face trials of many kinds, because you know that the testing of your faith develops perseverance. Perseverance must finish its work so that you may be mature and complete, not lacking anything."
—James 1:2-4

"Dear friends, do not be surprised at the painful trial you are suffering, as though something strange were happening to you. But rejoice that you participate in the sufferings of Christ, so that you may be overjoyed when his glory is revealed."
—1 Peter 4:12-13

Basic Truth
Effective college student leaders learn to handle conflict and criticism well.

Guided Prayer
Lord,
I love the ministry that I am a part of, but sometimes I don't want to be here at all. I don't like conflict, and I want to fight back when I'm criticized.

Help me find my way through all of this mess when I get all tangled up.

Amen.

Several years ago, I was college pastor at a church in California. I was experiencing a fruitful season in which our attendance, our budget, our ministry involvement, our conversions, and our excitement were going up each year. Everything seemed to be clicking—but why shouldn't it? This was a church, and most of these people were a part of the body of Christ.

Then things began to crumble. One of my student leaders had a disagreement with another leader in our department. Soon both leaders had attracted others to their point of view. Now there was a major faction in the ministry. I was on a summer trip as this conflict broke out and when I got home, I was greeted by a division in the college ministry. My first thought was, "These two student leaders are adults. They should be able to sort this thing out on their own." I was wrong. By the time I got involved, it was too late to salvage some of the students. One of the leaders left the group and took 30 others with him. They were angry. I was hurt.

I was totally taken by surprise. How could a group of people who claimed to know Christ end up hurting each other so deeply? The fact of the matter is, Jesus said, "In this world you will have trouble" (John 16:33). I certainly found out that being a Christian does not exempt me from the pain of disagreements and disappointments of this world. For the first time, I began to learn how to deal with conflict redemptively. I learned about leading when I would rather be leaving.

Parable of the Brawling Bride

Imagine for a moment you are at a wedding. The groom is up front looking more handsome than ever. The groomsmen are standing next to him, each hair in place, with their tuxedos pressed and looking sharp. Then the entire congregation stands and looks around to see the bride enter. They encounter a shocking sight. Instead of seeing an elegant, beautiful-looking bride, they see a bride whose dress is torn in numerous spots and whose hair is a mess, to say the least. She has a black eye, a fat lip, bruises all over her body, and blood stains on her dress...she looks pitiful. Can you imagine how the groom would feel with this image of his bride to greet him? Doesn't he deserve better than this?[1]

Sadly, this is often how we as Christians, the bride of Christ, come to Jesus. There is so much internal strife and conflict within the body of Christ that we look like the bride in the parable above. Doesn't Jesus deserve better than this?

It Will Come

No doubt you will experience some difficult and draining moments as a Christian collegian attempting to lead others. Leadership can be a thankless, lonely, and even discouraging task, simply because you are the one most responsible for the organization. You very likely will feel both affirmed and attacked as you lead people on the campus or even in the church.

The fact that both you and those you lead are humans means that you'll face some conflict and hurdles before the race is over. We are all sinful, which means none of us will do this relationship piece perfectly. And we all come from different backgrounds, mind-sets, and personalities, which means we won't always see eye-to-eye. In this session, we'll examine how to handle those difficult times with other people most effectively. We will learn how to deal with conflict so that we may grow and gain insight from it, rather than letting it leave us battered and bruised.

Reflect and Respond ...

Before we go any further, take a moment and reflect on some of the difficult situations you have faced in the past as a collegiate leader.

What are some conflicts you have faced? As a group, talk about them.

Do you see any patterns? Write these down.

If you are in a Covenant group like CrossSeekers, see if you can talk about the conflicts you have experienced individually in your accountability group.

Getting to the Source

In every conflict is an underlying reason for it. It usually is not simply about the issue you are arguing over. There is a source, according to James 4:1. Often the most common sources of conflict and difficulty with people are:
   ◆ Personality and relationship clashes
   ◆ Unspoken and unmet expectations
   ◆ Insecurity and identity issues
   ◆ Unresolved conflict from past wounds
   ◆ Independent attitudes and inflexible perspectives

Foundational Principles

To deal with the root of the problem, rather than the surface issue, here are some foundational principles I practice when faced with conflict:

1. Often, we must practice the 101 Percent Principle: find the 1 percent you can agree with, and give it 100 percent of your attention.

2. When the EMOTION expressed far outweighs the issue at hand, there is a HIDDEN issue to be faced.

3. In relationships, it is better to build a FENCE at the top of the cliff than a hospital at the bottom. Take precautions to prevent potential trouble.

4. As Christian campus leaders, we must initiate affirmation because many students struggle with INSECURITY and IDENTITY issues.

5. As Christian campus leaders, we must never place our EMOTIONAL HEALTH in the hands of someone else.

6. We must recognize that hurting people naturally HURT other people (students are not exempt).

7. We must embrace the ultimate biblical PRINCIPLE: If I can't get along with people, I can't get along with God.

The Bottom Line

First John 4:20 puts it this way:

"If anyone says, 'I love God,' yet hates his brother, he is a liar. For anyone who does not love his brother, whom he has seen, cannot love God, whom he has not seen."

God calls us to love one another, even when a person is difficult to love.

REMEMBER ...

Conflict is NORMAL.

It is going to happen because we are different.

Conflict is NEUTRAL.

It is neither destructive nor constructive in itself.

Conflict is NATURAL.

It is universal; you're not alone in your humanity.

"If anyone says, 'I love God,' yet hates his brother, he is a liar. For anyone who does not love his brother, whom he has seen, cannot love God, whom he has not seen" (1 John 4:20).

Porcupines and Noah's Ark

Years ago, Chuck Colson wrote a marvelous book called *The Body*. In it, he describes why we often experience conflict, even in the church where we're supposed to love everyone.

He compares the church to a bunch of porcupines on a cold night. We huddle together to get away from the cold, but when we do, we poke each other!

Later, he compares the church to Noah's ark. He asks the reader to imagine being on the ark. The minute we begin to hate the conditions, we think of the alternative—and stay put. He summarizes it this way: The stench on the inside would be unbearable if it weren't for the storm on the outside![2]

Eight Ways to Handle Criticism in a Healthy Way

Criticism comes with the territory of being a Christian leader. Here are some reminders on how to handle it successfully when it comes:

1. Understand the difference between constructive or destructive criticism.

2. Don't take yourself too seriously.

3. Look beyond the criticism and see the critic.

4. Recognize that good students get criticized.

5. Keep physically and spiritually in shape.

6. Don't just see the critic, see the crowd.

7. Wait for time to prove what is right.

8. Concentrate on your mission, change your mistakes. (We often do the opposite!)

Reflect and Respond ...

Reflect on what is your initial response to conflict. Briefly describe it here in a few words.

How do you normally handle it? (Check one.) Do you ❏ avoid it? ❏ face it head-on? Why did you check the box you did?

Think about what your natural conflict management style is. Can you describe some key elements here?

> The stench on the inside would be unbearable if it weren't for the storm on the outside!

A Biblical Example

The apostle Paul faced some conflict with a man named Philemon. The situation could have become awkward. Paul could see that they didn't see "eye-to-eye" concerning Onesimus, a runaway slave belonging to Philemon. Paul, no doubt, pondered the five options we all face when we get into a sticky relationship conflict:

1. **I'll get them!**—This approach is where one seeks retaliation as a recourse. The person who responds to conflict this way wants to get even. They have an "eye for an eye and a tooth for a tooth" mentality.

2. **I'll get out!**—The person who chooses this option for dealing with conflict merely wants to get out of the situation. They want to escape, so they avoid any further conflict.

3. **I'll give in!**—This person would rather give up than continue in any more conflict. This surrender is their means to a resolution.

4. **I'll go half!**—This person attempts to strike a deal to end the conflict. They try to agree on a compromise that both parties can live with.

5. **I'll deal with it!**—This person addresses the issue head-on. They attempt to understand the dynamics of what is going on and deal with the underlying issues.

The Book of Philemon

The following steps are the apostle Paul's course on conflict management. Read the Book of Philemon in the New Testament. Note how masterfully he communicates with Philemon, giving us a pattern to follow:

1. Compliment stage

"I always thank my God as I remember you in my prayers, because I hear about your faith in the Lord Jesus and your love for all the saints. I pray that you may be active in sharing your faith, so that you will have a full understanding of every good thing we have in Christ. Your love has given me great joy and encouragement, because you, brother, have refreshed the hearts of the saints" (Philem. 4-7).

Begin by focusing on the positive qualities. This may mean practicing the 101 Percent Principle: find the 1 percent you agree on or can affirm and give 100 percent of your attention to it.

2. Compromise stage

"Therefore, although in Christ I could be bold and order you to do what you ought to do, yet I appeal to you on the basis of love. I then, as Paul—an old man and now also a prisoner of Christ Jesus—I appeal to you for my son Onesimus, who became my son while I was in chains. Formerly he was useless to you, but now he has become useful both to you and to me. I am sending him—who is my very heart—back to you. I would have liked to keep him with me so that he could take your place in helping me while I am in chains for the gospel" (vv. 8-13).

Admit early that you are willing to assume some responsibility for the conflict. Recognize the differences in motivation, style, and temperament; meet them halfway.

3. Choice stage

"But I did not want to do anything without your consent, so that any favor you do will be spontaneous and not forced" (v. 14).

Group Up

When you are faced with conflict in your campus group or on a campus life issue related to a great number of students, how do you handle it? Discuss it in your group.

Next, lay out the choice in front of you both, as you understand it. Maintain their dignity if possible. You can flee it, fight it, or face it. Take any steps possible to sustain friendship.

4. Challenge stage

"Perhaps the reason he was separated from you for a little while was that you might have him back for good—no longer as a slave, but better than a slave, as a dear brother. He is very dear to me but even dearer to you, both as a man and as a brother in the Lord. So if you consider me a partner, welcome him as you would welcome me. If he has done you any wrong or owes you anything, charge it to me. I, Paul, am writing this with my own hand. I will pay it back—not to mention that you owe me your very self. I do wish, brother, that I may have some benefit from you in the Lord; refresh my heart in Christ" (vv. 15-20).

Commit yourself verbally to steps you will take with that individual on campus or in your church group, then extend a clear challenge and await their response. Remember the axiom: friends may come and go, but enemies accumulate. Lay out good boundaries and parameters to keep things healthy. This is Covenant Living at its best.

5. Confidence stage

"Confident of your obedience, I write to you, knowing that you will do even more than I ask. And one thing more: Prepare a guest room for me, because I hope to be restored to you in answer to your prayers" (vv. 21-22).

Finally, end by expressing sincere confidence in them. Let them know you trust them to make the right decision(s) and nothing will prevent you from loving them. Remember, it is more important to win a "soul" than to win an argument.

Group Up
Do you think these steps from Philemon are important for you as a campus leader? Why or why not?

Reflect and Respond ...

Recall if there are any foundational principles that you already practice like the ones above? Can you recall certain scenarios? Briefly describe them in the space below.

Have they helped to reduce or resolve conflict in the past? How?

Give Them Something to Do

When I was a pastor in San Diego, a young lady named Robin was part of our church family. Robin desperately wanted to have a position on our collegiate council, which was the governing board of the college department. I was hesitant to give her any position. Robin wasn't emotionally healthy. She did things just to get attention and often sabotaged her own success. She just wasn't the kind of person I wanted on our council.

Each week when she asked me if she could have a position, I would beat around the bush, and make up some excuse on how we didn't have any more positions to fill. This went on for months, until I finally told myself the truth. I wasn't doing her any favors by being dishonest with her. Every week I dug a deeper hole, making up new excuses to prevent her from getting a position. So I decided to ask myself the question: what would Robin have to do in order to be ready to fill a position on the council?

I came up with four significant action items, including getting some counseling at a local Christian counseling center. When she inquired the next Sunday about the position again, I was ready. I said to her, "Robin, I'll be honest with you. I would love to see you on that council, if you were ready for it. Let me give you four things you can do to prepare for it. If you will do these four things, I will nominate you for a position. I mean that."

Robin smiled. She finally had some tangible things to do to reach her goal. What's more, I actually meant every word I said. If she got healthy, I had no reason to keep her off the council. But the greatest benefit for both of us was this: the next Sunday when she came to me again and asked about the position, I could say to her, "Have you done the four things I spoke to you about?"

When she said, "Not yet," I could say, "Well, come back to me when you have them done. Then we can talk about your position." This was a simple step that gave both of us hope and direction. Effective confrontation always includes measurable action steps.

Biblical Confrontation

When someone under your care (for example, in a covenant group) has done an apparent wrong, the Bible calls us to confront them when the issue is clear: sin, failure to keep a public commitment, a destructive attitude, harmful conversation, and so forth. If you waver on whether the Bible is clear on this subject, review these passages:

2 Corinthians 10:4-5
The tools of our trade are divinely powerful to challenge people's thinking.

1 Thessalonians 5:14
Remind, warn, admonish, and encourage the faint-hearted.

2 Timothy 3:16
Scripture is profitable for teaching, reproof, correction, and training.

2 Timothy 4:2-4
Preach, reprove, rebuke, and exhort.

Colossians 1:28
Admonish (warn by reminding) people.

Titus 1:13
Reprove severely that they may be sound in faith.

Remember, your goal is to see them transformed by the power of God. *Your objective is not condemnation, but restoration.* Students must know we love them, but we love truth more than anything else in the world. An unexamined life is not worth living. Would you like more information to form a Covenant group that has spiritual accountability as a key element? At the back of this book, you are given information on how to receive information related to CrossSeekers and Covenant Living. Check it out.

"Dear friends, do not be surprised at the painful trial you are suffering, as though something strange were happening to you. But rejoice that you participate in the sufferings of Christ, so that you may be overjoyed when his glory is revealed" (1 Pet. 4:12-13).

I Need You, Jim

John Maxwell tells the story of his days as a pastor in Ohio. A 65-year-old man named Jim was the most influential man in the church. Unfortunately, he was extremely negative. He had run off the last two pastors and his attitude affected the atmosphere of the whole church.

So when Pastor Maxwell arrived, he arranged a meeting with Jim. In that meeting, John said to him: "Jim, I have heard that you have a lot of influence in this church. I've also heard that you have been very negative about the last two pastors. That's why I wanted to meet with you right away to make an offer to you. For the next few years, you will have more influence than me in this church. During that time, you can make things horrible for me as a young pastor. We can fight and argue until I eventually win enough new people to Christ and invite enough new people to this church that I begin to have as much influence as you. Then I'll begin to win some of those fights. The future of this church will sway back and forth at that point. We will make each other miserable.

"Jim, it looks to me like you have a choice in front of you. You can literally spend the last years of your life fighting with me, or you can accept my invitation to you. My offer is, let's work together. I will meet with you every Tuesday and discuss the issues of the church. I will get your counsel on everything. Together, we can make these next years the most fruitful years in our church's history. I need you, Jim. The choice is yours."

Jim simply got up and walked out the door. Pastor Maxwell followed him, not knowing if he was leaving for good. Jim stopped at the drinking fountain and got a drink for what seemed like an eternity. When he stood up, his face was red. Tears were streaming down his cheeks. He looked at John Maxwell and gave him a huge bear hug. Then he said, "You can count on me, Pastor. I'm in your corner."

Jim was a changed man after that. People in the church wondered what had happened to him. I'll tell you what happened. Jim met a leader who had the character, security, and humility to confront him in a redemptive way.[3]

Reflect and Respond ...

Reflect and think if you have ever had to confront someone on an issue. How did you approach the person? What happened? To crystallize your thoughts, jot them down in the space provided.

What do you find most difficult when confronting someone? Jot down some keys words. For example, you may find "controlling anger" the most difficult thing.

> "I'll tell you what happened. Jim met a leader who had the character, security, and humility to confront him in a redemptive way."
>
> Is it important for you as a leader on campus to be redemptive in difficult situations? Why? Why not?

Steps Toward Effective Confrontation

No one likes to deal with confrontation, but it will be necessary as a Christian leader to know how to do it effectively. Here are steps you can take toward effective confrontation.

1. **Pray through your own anger.**—Don't let emotion lead you. Wait until you're objective, but deal with issues in your group or with another individual before they grow into "big ones."

2. **You initiate the contact.**—Don't wait for the other person to initiate. Scripture beckons you to make things right whether you are the offender or the offended.

3. **Begin with affirmation.**—Speak words of love and encouragement first. Then receive fresh permission to challenge that roommate or whoever it may be on campus or in your church, and be honest about what you see.

4. **Tell them that you have a problem or struggle.**—Don't say it's their problem, but yours. Own the fact that you have wrestled through dealing with the issue. Not doing this may mean that you will always be doing someone else's chores in the dorm suite.

5. **Bring up the issue and explain that you don't understand what's happened.**—The meeting may be more of a "clarification" than a confrontation. Give them the benefit of the doubt and allow them to explain themselves. Be loving and clear. Aim to clarify.

6. **Listen and allow them to respond.**—At this point, you must stop talking and let them respond. They may present a new perspective that in the end will help you both.

7. **Establish forgiveness and repentance, if necessary.**—Connect the issue you are correcting with who they are in Christ. Don't conclude the meeting until forgiveness is extended and issues are clear and resolved.

8. **Compromise on opinions, but not on biblical convictions or principles.**—Determine what you will "die for." Be flexible with your own opinions or preferences, but not on issues where the Bible has clearly spoken. Covenant living is based on biblical principles.

9. **Pray and affirm your love as you close your time together.**—Always close these times with prayer. Give them hope for the future and remind them of their place in God's heart and yours. Help them never to question that they are loved.

Pass the Blessings, Please!

Let's shift gears and talk about a deeper issue. Personally, I believe the primary reason people experience unresolved conflict and difficulties is that they are hungry for "the blessing." In the Old Testament, men would give a "blessing" to their children; similarly, rabbis would "bless" their students, and craftsmen would mentor and bless their apprentices. The "blessing" consists of:

- **Affirming words**
  We need our friends and others to speak words of encouragement and affirmation.

- **Meaningful touch**
  We need to be embraced and touched by others.

Service: Something done out of an experience of grace. It's a loving response to a new identity in order to say thank you to God.

- **Expression of high value**

  We need to know the importance and value we add to others.

- **Description of special features**

  We need someone to believe in us and our potential.

- **Application of genuine commitment**

  We need to know a friend or a member of our covenant group is going to stand by us.[4]

Often we cannot put words to it, but we are like Jacob. We wrestle all of our lives to get the "blessing" (Gen. 32:24-26). As fallen people, we have lost our security and sense of significance. In a very real sense, this may explain why so many seem to have lost their sense of identity. Hence, we tend to struggle to meet personal needs in an unhealthy way.

Give the Blessing

Colleen was a beautiful young lady who visited our church one Sunday. We could tell she had never attended before, but she kept coming, and seemed to soak up the fellowship and the hugs. After eight weeks, we discovered the power of "the blessing" in her life. She revealed her past on an unforgettable Sunday morning.

As I taught on "The Blessing," Colleen stood and walked down to the front of the auditorium. I continued speaking, but realized she was there because she wanted to say something. Usually, it is not my custom to turn the microphone over to someone who spontaneously walks forward. But somehow this time, it seemed like the right thing to do. I was so glad I did. Colleen collected herself and began to speak. After stumbling around a bit, she confessed that she was a dancer in a gentlemen's club downtown. She took her clothes off each evening on the stage and went home with a different man almost every time. Through tears she acknowledged this was the only way she had ever before experienced love. She paused. Now she said things were different. In our church, she had found something new. She talked about how she had received this "blessing" for the first time in her life. It certainly never came from her home when she was growing up. The love, the words of encouragement, the hugs, the acceptance, and the belief in her potential were more than she could fathom. She then said, "I am quitting my job tomorrow. I don't need it anymore."

There wasn't a dry eye in the building. Everyone in that auditorium had seen first-hand what happens when someone receives the blessing from healthy relationships. I, for one, have never forgotten what Colleen taught us.

Reflect and Respond ...

After reading the Scripture and considering what the "blessing" consists of, think of ten ways you can pass on the blessing. In the space below, list ten ways.

1.

2.

3.

4.

5.

6.

7.

8.

9.

10.

Do you know someone who needs the blessing? Write their names in the margin and commit to doing one of the items you came up with. Do it NOW. Don't wait! You may not know how much these people need to be blessed and encouraged.

Inner Health

What constitutes being a healthy, well-adjusted person? Note the following four components for inner health and well-being.

1. A sense of WORTH—if this is missing, we feel inferior.

2. A sense of BELONGING—if this is missing, we feel insecure.

3. A sense of COMPETENCE—if this is missing, we feel inadequate.

4. A sense of PURPOSE—if this is missing, we feel illegitimate.

Spotting the Symptoms

How do you know when someone needs to be blessed? If someone is searching for the "blessing," one or more of the following symptoms generally shows up in their life in a deep way:

Hostile spirit	Independent	Overcompensation
Ungrateful spirit	Fearful or anxious	Inexpressive
Oversensitive/Self-conscious	Driven spirit	Co-dependent
	Tendency to sabotage self	

People attempt to meet the need for security and significance through many "artificial" means. You may recognize some of the big ones below:

Performance	Power	Prestige
Possessions	Pleasure	People

Our behavior
is always
based on
meeting
some need.

What I View as My Source Will Determine My Course

The diagram below illustrates an important truth. Our behavior is always based on meeting some need. Further, it is motivated by certain assumptions. In the circles below, notice how it all begins at the top, with a need. This leads to motivation, which reveals what our basic assumptions are. For example, if I sense a need for love from others, I may become motivated to pursue relationships with the opposite sex. If I begin to engage in sexual immorality, you can guess my basic assumption: I must sleep around to get the love that I want.

Unfortunately, if you continue to see where the circles lead, you find it leads to driven behavior, obstacles, and reaching a goal—only to find temporary satisfaction. Ultimately, we become empty again and begin the vicious circle all over. This type of emptiness can be seen all over campus. Most students lack covenant living in their lives. As a Christian leader, examine your response to the needs on your campus.

This is how most people live their lives: driven behavior, temporary solutions, emptiness. Remember: what you view as your source will determine your course.

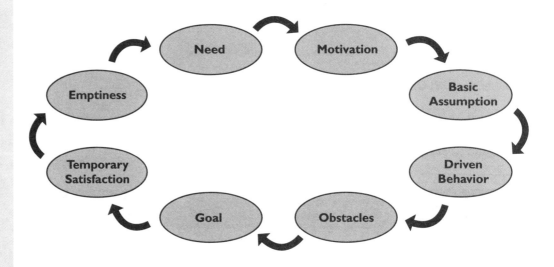

Reflect and Respond ...

What is determining your course? As you evaluate needs that you have, what basic assumptions lie behind them that could lead you to follow this vicious cycle? How will you address these from a biblical perspective? Even if you need to discuss this with a friend in your campus group, see if you can identify ten ways to address the needs biblically. List as many as you can.

1.

2.

3.

4.

5.

6.

7.

8.

9.

10.

Are there other students you observe around you who are following this cycle?
❏ Yes ❏ No ❏ I'm not sure

What needs do they exhibit?

What basic assumptions may be behind these needs?

How can you help address these so others on campus might not continue to fall into this unhealthy pattern of behavior?

> If we see the big picture of what God is trying to accomplish in our lives, we can better cooperate with God in the process.

The Root and Fruit of Behavior

The diagram below will help you visualize what happens when a student experiences inward conflict. We used it in the first book dealing with collegiate leadership entitled *Authentic Influence: Leading Without Titles* when we dealt with our personal security.

Like a weed growing above the ground, you can visibly see the student's negative behavior and habits. They have a pattern of destructive behavior. If you look just beneath the surface, it doesn't take long to discover negative attitudes and emotions. When you dig further, however, you see there is often an issue of unforgiveness. Much of the time, a student experiencing conflict has someone they need to forgive from a past issue. It is either themselves or someone else.

If you dig further, you can usually discover the need that was never met in the student's life. Often, this is associated with the person they have not forgiven.

Keep digging and you often find that the root issue is personal worth. These unmet needs ultimately stem from a sense of unworthiness. This is why giving and receiving the blessing is so important (p. 112). When we establish a person's worth, we are addressing the root of the problem. Jesus did this at the cross. His death is the ultimate statement of our value. "While we were still sinners, Christ died for us" (Rom. 5:8).

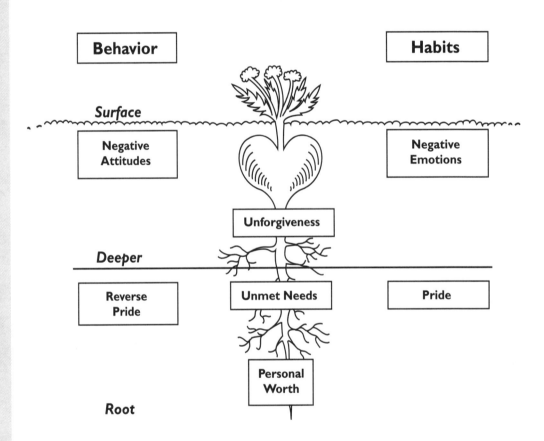

Reflect and Respond ...

Do you know students on campus or others in your church who exhibit symptoms of a deeper problem stemming from a lack of self-worth? (Check one that applies for you.)
❑ Yes ❑ No ❑ Everywhere ❑ Not sure

How did you normally handle their behavior? Jot down a word or phrase describing what you did or did not do.

From what you have learned in this chapter, list three ways to show how will you handle them differently as a Christian leader growing in Christ.

1.

2.

3.

Bringing It All Home

Miss Thompson had just begun to teach third grade. In her first year, she had a troubled student named Teddy Stollard. He was sort of her initiation to the teaching profession. Teddy was rebellious, distracting to the other students, and always found ways to get attention. It didn't matter whether it was negative or positive. Miss Thompson responded with lots of time-outs and discipline. She was so frustrated with him, at times she could hardly wait until Christmas break just to be away from him.

On their last day before Christmas break, the class celebrated with a party. Some of the kids brought Miss Thompson gifts. Teddy brought two. When she opened his, they drew giggles from his classmates. The first was a string of pearls—half of the pearls were missing. The second was a bottle of half-used perfume. To prevent a further disruption, Miss Thompson quieted the giggles by trying on the necklace and applying the perfume. She told Teddy how much she liked them and that she was proud to wear them.

When the bell rang, all the kids left except for Teddy. He remained to say something to Miss Thompson. It was their first serious conversation all year. "Miss Thompson," he mumbled. "I'm really glad you like the pearls. Ummm, you look just like my mom used to look." There was a pause. "And Miss Thompson, I'm glad you like the perfume, too. You smell just like my mom." Then he walked out of the room.

She suddenly realized she needed to check Teddy's files in the office to find out what was going on at home. Come to think of it, she hadn't seen Teddy's mom all year. When she examined his file, it all made sense. When Teddy was in kindergarten, his mother had gotten very sick. By the time he was in first grade, she was bedridden. She had died while he was in the second grade. Now Teddy was trying to cope with life without a mother.

Miss Thompson hit her knees and prayed, "God, forgive me for being so blind. Help me to bless this young boy, come January. Give me wisdom to know when to discipline and when to hug. Amen."

January was a transforming month. As Miss Thompson gave Christian love to Teddy, he responded in a grand fashion. He stopped being so rebellious. He wasn't a distraction anymore. In fact, by the end of the semester, he became a model student. He even helped Miss Thompson after class by erasing the chalkboard. When the school year ended, Teddy did his best to thank Miss Thompson for what she did.

Years went by and Miss Thompson taught many more third-grade classes. She did her best to remember the lesson of Teddy Stollard. It became easy about a decade later. Teddy wrote her this note:

Dear Miss Thompson,
I just wanted you to know, I graduated from high school today. I bet you thought I could never do that. Thank you for helping me through the third grade. You are the reason I made it this far.
Love, Teddy Stollard

Needless to say, she saved the letter. Four years later she got another one:

Dear Miss Thompson,
I just wanted to write and tell you, I graduated from college today, second in my class. I bet you thought I could never do that. Thank you for helping me through the third grade. I would not have made it without you.
Love, Teddy Stollard

Five years later, Miss Thompson got her third and final letter from Teddy:

Dear Miss Thompson,
I wanted to write you and tell you I am now Theodore Stollard, M.D. I graduated from medical school today, first in my class. I bet you thought I could never do that. I wanted to thank you again for making such a difference in my life when I was nine years old. You are the reason I made it here.

One other thing, Miss Thompson. This summer, I am getting married. I wondered if you would be willing to come and sit where my mother would have sat in the ceremony. I can't think of anyone I would rather have sit there. Please write and tell me if you can.

Love, Teddy Stollard

Miss Thompson did take part in Teddy's wedding. It was a milestone and a reminder of the difference someone can make when they choose to give a Christian blessing to someone else. The one who deserves it least is often the one who needs it the most.[5]

Assess Yourself

Reflect on various situations in which you have been involved in conflict with other students or someone in your church or community. What have you learned in this chapter about yourself and how you typically manage conflict? Journal in the space allowed some of your thoughts and actions.

As a Christian leader on campus, what do you need to change or work on to begin handling conflict more effectively? Space is once again provided for you to journal your thoughts.

Guided Prayer
Lord,
under no circumstances am I happy that problems arise at times in my ministry on campus and in the church.

But I am glad that all who are involved can grow through it.

Don't let me give up on them, just like You never give up on me.

Amen.

We have seen that one effective way to deal with difficult people is to bless them. Usually their difficult behavior stems for some unseen need that is not being met.

How do you plan to begin passing the blessing? List some thoughts in this space.

Application

Every leader wants to quit at one time or another. That's just part of being a leader. We need to lead with the understanding that no one is perfect; not you, not me. It may also be helpful for your team or covenant group to realize that simple truth. Next time a problem arises, utilize a few of the steps in this lesson. That way you can be the best leader possible.

Footnotes

Session 1

[1]Dowley, Tim, *Eerdman's Handbook to the History of Christianity* (Guidepost Publishers, Carmel, NY: 1977).

Session 2

[1]Maxwell, John C., *Developing the Leader Within You* (Thomas Nelson, Nashville: 1993) 17-19.

[2]Verne, Jules, *The Mysterious Island* (Penguin Putnum, New York: 1993) 93.

[3]Maxwell, John C., *Developing the Leader Within You* (Thomas Nelson, Nashville: 1993) 21-22.

[4]Ibid., p. 28.

[5]"Curious Beginnings," *Strange Stories & Amazing Facts* (Readers Digest Association, Inc., Pleasantville, NY: 1976) 522.

[6]Maxwell, p. 29.

[7]Sculley, John and Byrne, John A., *Odyssey: Pepsi to Apple* (Harper Trade, New York: 2000).

Session 3

[1]*Country People Magazine,* February/March 1994, 30-31.

[2]Maxwell, John C., *One Team, Team Won,* INJOY Life Club Tape, Volume 4, Number 11 (INJOY, Inc., Atlanta: 1989).

[3]Wooden, John, *They Call Me Coach* (NTC Publishing, Chicago: 1988) 107.

[4]Webber, Stu, *Locking Arms: God's Design for Masculine Friendships* (Questar Publishers, Sisters, OR: 1995) 78.

Session 4

[1]Maxwell, John C., *Planning Pays,* INJOY Life Club Tape, Volume 9, No. 8 (INJOY, Inc., Atlanta: 1994).

[2]Maxwell, John C., *Think On These Things* (Beacon Hill, Kansas City, MO: 1980) 83-85.

[3]Ibid., p. 65.

Session 5

[1]Wills, Gary, *Certain Trumpets: The Call of Leaders* (Simon and Schuster Trade, New York: 1994).

[2]Ailes, Roger and Kraushar, Jon, *You are the Message: Getting What You Want by Being Who You Are* (Doubleday, New York: 1996) 6.

[3]Ibid., p. 11.

[4]Ibid., p. 38.

[5]Humes, James C., *The Sir Winston Method: Five Secrets of Speaking the Language of Leadership* (Morrow, William and Co., New York: 1991) 96.

Session 6

[1]Clinton, J. Robert, *Leadership Emergence Theory* (Barnabas Resources, Altadena, CA: 1989) 387-389.

[2]Maxwell, John C., *21 Irrefutable Laws Of Leadership* (Nelson Publishing, Nashville: 1998) 121.

[3]Ibid., p. 129.

[4]Winchester, C J, *John Wesley: The Methodist* (Eaton Mains Publishers, New York: 1903) 88.

Session 7

[1]George, Carl and Logan, Robert, *Leading and Managing Your Church* (Fleming Revell, Old Tappan, NJ: 1987) 18.

[2]Maxwell, John C., *How To Stay Away From Bored Meetings,* Injoy Life Club Tape, Volume 5, Number 12 (INJOY, Inc., Atlanta: 1991).

Session 8

[1]Mains, Karen, *With My Whole Heart* (Multnomah Publishers, Sisters, OR: 1994) 41.

[2]Colson, Chuck, *The Body: Being Light in Darkness* (W Publishing Group, Nashville, TN: 1992).

[3]Maxwell, John C., *21 Irrefutable Laws Of Leadership,* 133.

[4]Trent, John and Smalley, Gary, *The Blessing* (Simon and Schuster, New York: 1991) 66.

[5]Campolo, Anthony, *Who Switched the Price Tags?* (W Publishing Group, Nashville: 1986).

Skills to Lead Others

Hopefully, as you have studied each session in this book, you have watched yourself growing as a Christian leader on your campus and in your church. Even if you are able to memorize every word in this book, there will be a need for you to continue growing in your leadership skills as you relate to others. This book, the second designed for collegiate leadership, has focused on "skills to lead others." In the first book, *Authentic Influence: Leading without Titles,* I sought more to help Christian students, like yourself, understand the importance of developing the foundation for leadership. From "God Never Calls a Wrong Number" to "You Can Be a People Person: Cultivating Your Relational Skills," we realize that developing a positive Christian leadership style is a journey. If you missed this one, you may want to see if your covenant group can go through it as well.

Your journey is not over. Hopefully, however, this book has given you some clear direction. You have the "skills" before you. With our blessing, go and be the Christian leader on your campus and in your church God desires you to be. Know that God is always with you.
Let Him direct your path.

On the remaining pages, you will find discover more about EQUIP, based in Atlanta, Georgia, and STUDENT MINISTRY PUBLISHING and NATIONAL COLLEGIATE MINISTRY of LifeWay Christian Resources, based in Nashville, Tennessee.

You will also find additional collegiate resources you may want to use as your covenant lifestyle continues to grow. If you want to know more about Covenant Living, these resources can speak to this need for you as a student on campus.

A Word About
EQUIP

EQUIP is a non-profit Christian organization devoted to the development of Christ-like leaders in the most influential and neglected places of our world. We believe that everything rises and falls on leadership. We partner with ministries, churches, and schools in three key areas: the international community, the urban community, and among students in the academic community. This collegiate workbook is part of our partnership in the academic arena.

Developing leaders among college students allows us to invest in tomorrow's leaders today. Here are a few of the resources that we currently offer:

• Leadership Conferences
The Leadership Forums are 1-2 day training events tailor-made to the needs of your campus ministry. They can be profiled as outreach events on your campus for fraternities, sororities, RA's, student government, and more. The conferences serve as a catalyst to build hunger for further personal leadership development.

• Mentoring Groups
The Leadership Exchange contains a year's worth of leadership cassette tapes, taught by Dr. John C. Maxwell, to spark discussion and application in monthly mentoring groups. In addition to the tapes, student handbooks and facilitator's guides are provided. Along with this tool, we offer "Portrait of a Leader," a series of discussion guides on leadership. Our hope is to provide support, interaction, accountability, and to foster a leadership culture within your ministry through these tools.

• Video Curriculum
The Leadership Journey is designed to furnish ongoing, systematic leadership training for students. The video curriculum is divided into 72 12-minute segments to be viewed in class and then discussed. The lectures cover the "21 Irrefutable Laws of Leadership" and are taught by Dr. John C. Maxwell and Dr. Tim Elmore. It is crafted to be used in a classroom setting along with assignments and reading.

• Resources
The Leadership Library represents a fourth component in our partnership. EQUIP offers a battery of books, tapes, videos, and training manuals for leaders and potential leaders to enhance your leadership growth. The resources cover subjects including leadership, mentoring, spiritual growth, people skills, priorities, vision, staff development, and more. These have been discounted for campus workers and college students.

• Leadership Academy
The Leadership Academy is a two-week institute for student interns. It is designed to develop leadership qualities and skills through adventure learning, reading, interviews, field trips, mentors, small groups, and equipping seminars. For information, check out our Web site at *www.leadership-academy.org*.

Visit EQUIP at *www.growingleaders.com*

A Word About
Collegiate Ministries

Collegiate Ministries is an arm of LifeWay Christian Resources of the Southern Baptist Convention. Our work is done in joint partnership between the areas of Ministry Team Leadership and Student Ministry Publishing. With over 80 years of ministry on the college campus, our ministry speaks to and for hundreds of thousands college students each year. We have five main objectives in ministering to collegians. They are: Bible study; Evangelism; Leadership Development; Transformational Discipleship, and Christian service.

A spiritual strategy we use to develop collegiate leaders in churches and campus programs is called CrossSeekers.

CrossSeekers Covenant Living

Collegians across the country are taking the pledge to covenant living. Students are seeking to develop spiritual lives which exhibit the six CrossSeeker Covenant points. These are:

Integrity: I will seek to be a person of integrity (2 Timothy 2:15).
My attitudes and actions reveal my commitment to live the kind of life Christ modeled for me—to speak the truth in love, to stand firm in my convictions, and to be honest and trustworthy.

Witness: I will seek to speak and live a relevant, authentic, and consistent witness (1 Peter 3:15).
I will tell others the story of how Jesus changed my life, and I will seek to live a radically changed life each day. I will share the good news of Jesus Christ with courage and boldness.

Spiritual Growth: I will seek to pursue consistent spiritual growth (Colossians 2:6-7).
The Christian life is a continuing journey, and I am committed to a consistent, personal relationship with Jesus Christ, to faithful study of His Word, and to regular corporate spiritual growth through the ministry of the New Testament church.

I will seek opportunities to serve in Christ's name (Luke 4:18-19).
I believe that God desires to draw all people into a loving, redeeming relationship with Him. As His disciple, I will give myself to be His hands to reach others in ministry and missions.

I will seek to honor my body as the temple of God, dedicated to a lifestyle of purity (1 Corinthians 6:19-20).
Following the example of Christ, I will keep my body healthy and strong, avoiding temptations and destructive personal vices. I will honor the gift of life by keeping myself sexually pure and free from addictive drugs.

I will seek to be godly in all things, Christlike in all relationships (Colossians 3:12-14).
In every relationship and in every situation, I will seek to live as Christ would. I will work to heal brokenness, to value each person as a child of God, to avoid petty quarrels and harsh word, to let go of bitterness and resentment that hinder genuine Christian love.

CrossSeeker Resources

For each point of the covenant, we have Christian resources written for the covenant for college students. To obtain a catalog of these resources, call 1-615-251-2783. To order a CrossSeeker resource, call 1-800-458-2772; fax 615-251-5933; email: *customerservice@lifeway.com* or visit the LifeWay Christian Store serving you.

CrossSeekers information

If you have questions relating to CrossSeekers Covenant Living, contact us at 615-251-2783.

CrossSeekers Resources

CrossSeekers: Discipleship Covenant for a New Generation
by Henry Blackaby and Richard Blackaby

Discover the six CrossSeekers principles brought to life in a user-friendly, practical, story-telling format. This study sets the stage for an exploration of each CrossSeekers Covenant point. Biblical and contemporary examples of promises made, promises kept, and promises broken, along with consequences, bring the biblical truths home to today's college students.
◆ 9 sessions ◆ Interactive in format ◆ Leader's helps included ◆ $8.95 ◆ ISBN 0-7673-9084-9

CrossSeekers: Transparent Living, Living a Life of Integrity *by Rod Handley*

Integrity. Everyone talks about it. God *delights* in it. We *demand* it. But what exactly *is* integrity, and is it important? If you want to be a person of integrity, to live the kind of life Christ modeled—to speak the truth in love, to stand firm in your convictions, to be honest and trustworthy, then *Transparent Living, Living a Life of Integrity* is for you! This study supports the CrossSeekers Covenant principle *integrity.* ◆ 6 sessions ◆ Leader's guide included ◆ $6.95 ◆ ISBN 0-7673-9296-5

CrossSeekers: The Challenge—Transforming the World Through Covenant Living *by David Edwards*

LifeWay offers your church lots of ways to reach students who are not only seeking to fully develop themselves academically, but develop a personal relationship with Christ as well. Written by popular collegiate speaker and teacher Dave Edwards, this resource is designed to take collegians through eight interactive sessions of moving deeper spiritually into covenant living as a CrossSeeker.
◆ 8 sessions ◆ $7.95 ◆ ISBN 0-7673-9295-7

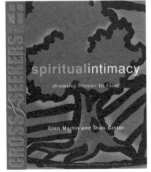

CrossSeekers: Spiritual Intimacy, Drawing Closer to God
by Glen Martin and Dian Ginter

Spiritual Intimacy will intensify the desire of your heart to know God more intimately, will help you realize where you are in the process of drawing closer to God, and will show you how to move ahead by knowing God on six successive levels. This study supports the CrossSeekers covenant point *spiritual growth.*
◆ 6 sessions ◆ Interactive in format ◆ Leader's guide included ◆ $6.95
◆ ISBN 0-7673-9427-5

CrossSeekers: Holy and Acceptable, Building a Pure Temple

by Dave Edwards

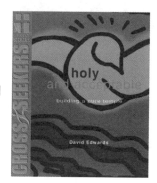

First Corinthians 6 tells us that our bodies are temples of the Holy Spirit. But what does that mean and why should we care? This study looks at what it means for us to be God's temple. Through Bible study and contemporary situations, the physical, mental, and spiritual aspects are explored, along with their interrelatedness, as well as what to do when you fail in your pursuit of purity. This study supports the CrossSeekers Covenant principle *purity*. ◆ 6 sessions ◆ Interactive in format ◆ Leader's guide included ◆ $6.95 ◆ ISBN 0-7673-9428-3

CrossSeekers: Fearless, Sharing an Authentic Witness

by William Fay and Dean Finley

Fearless, Sharing an Authentic Witness equips collegians for sharing their faith with others. Sessions address concepts such as our lives as a living witness (using the CrossSeekers Covenant points for discussion), how Jesus shared with persons He met, learning where God is at work in another person's life, a threat-free and effective method for presenting the gospel, and addressing difficult questions/situations. Based on *Share Jesus Without Fear,* this study supports the CrossSeekers Covenant principle *witness*. ◆ 6 sessions ◆ Interactive in format ◆ Leader's guide included ◆ $6.95 • ISBN 0-7673-9865-3

CrossSeekers: Virtuous Reality, Becoming the Ideal Woman

by Vicki Courtney

Virtuous Reality challenges college women to become ideal women as defined by God's standards, rather than the world's standards. The primary Bible passage that forms the foundation of the book is Proverbs 31, which describes a virtuous woman with worth far above rubies. Sessions of the book attempt to dispel the world's definition of the ideal woman. They address key qualities of a virtuous woman, and emphasize the importance of college women basing their worth solely on Christ. Sessions also challenge women to pursue wisdom, discern folly, develop a healthy perspective on dating, and discover their God-given purpose in life. ◆ 6 sessions ◆ Leader's guide included ◆ $6.95 ◆ ISBN 0-6330-0455-3

Transitions: Preparing for College

compiled by Art Herron

For high school juniors and seniors *and their parents.* Practical help for the transition from high school to college—the admissions process, financial aid, loans and scholarships, lifestyle changes, spiritual development, and more!
◆ 6 sessions ◆ Leader's helps included ◆ $7.95 ◆ ISBN 0-7673-9082-2

To order call 1-800-458-2772.